"This book was not what I was expecting. It was so much better! It is a life-changer! Lisa says, 'allowing God to renew our mind is the beginning of a continuous and ongoing transformation.' And through sacrifice of my body and mind I become a reflection of Him. This is not just a book of trite suggestions on how to take better care of yourself. This is a deep look at yourself and the choices you make. And at the heart of it all is God's purpose and your relationship with Him. A definite must-read in your path to spiritual wellness."

Susan Edmonds, Nixa, MO

"Lisa has taken the self-care concept from a Biblical perspective encouraging us to pursue Christ and the eternal matters instead of focusing on the temporary fallen world."

Ifeoma Samuel

"I have really enjoyed reading this book and being challenged in my walk with God to take on self-care! I have learned a lot about how self-care is important, and the book has really spoken to me with things I deal with in my own life. I struggle with anxiety and making sure everything is done and perfect. I have tried to cut back on this, especially with having a daughter and wanting/needing to spend time with her. I am making it a goal to spend more time focusing on being present with her and also to be more present with God. This book was encouraging because it really showed me that I was not alone in my struggles and that others have the same struggles."

Danielle Hartsell, RN, Nixa, MO

"This is a book every care-giver or ministry person needs to read. It provides a fresh perspective of the burdens we carry and suggests a change of focus towards our own self-care. This involves a radical shift to viewing such self-care as not being self-centered but rather centered on God as an act of worship to our Creator. The ideas in support of this are developed logically and cogently. The appealing thing about the book is its engaging and conversational tone with snippets of your own experience in areas the reader can identify with."

Fleur Vaz, Freelance writer and editor, Malaysia

"The book has a smooth flow and is easy to read/understand. The examples you use are relatable. I have been intrigued by some connections you have made to scripture that I have never thought of before! For example, how self-care is like an offering (sacrifice) to the Lord. And how the process of sacrifice in the Old Testament is attached to health and wellness. I get a new concept every time I read more."

Pamela Stafford, Springfield, MO

THE SELF-CARE IMPACT

Motivation and Inspiration for Wellness

by Lisa Kimrey, RN

Scripture quotations taken from The Holy Bible, New International Version®
NIV®
Copyright © 1973 1978 1984 2011 by Biblica, Inc. TM
Used by permission. All rights reserved worldwide.

Scripture quotations marked (NLT) are taken from the Holy Bible, New Living Translation, copyright © 1996, 2004, 2007, 2013, 2015 by Tyndale House Foundation. Used by permission of Tyndale House Publishers, Inc., Carol Stream, Illinois 60188. All rights reserved.

ISBN: 978-1-7348056-0-4 (ebook)
ISBN: 978-1-7348056-1-1 (paperback)

Editor: Fleur Vaz
Forward by: Jim Stovall
Cover Design: Angie at Pro_ebookcovers

This book may contain affiliate links, marked (affiliate link).

Be Sure to Download Your
FREE Bible Study Checklist
& Workbook

https://mylifenurse.com/self-
care-impact-free-checklist/

Dedication

This book is dedicated to my family. I thank God for you.

To my wonderful husband Richard, thank you for supporting my dreams; you are my Prince Charming. To my children, Joshua and Sara, thank you for always cheering me on; you both bring tremendous joy to my life. To my mom, Dianna, thank you for always believing I could do whatever I wanted to do. And, to my dad, Merle, thank you for teaching me to never give up. I love you all so much.

Table of Contents

Foreword

As the author of over 40 books myself, having 8 of them turned into motion pictures, I'm embarrassed to admit to the readers of the foreword to this wonderful book, that when I could read with my eyes, as you are doing now, I don't know that I ever read a whole book cover-to-cover. As a blind person now, for over 30 years, thanks to high-speed digital audio, I am able to complete an audio book virtually every day. Becoming a reader made me want to become a writer, and becoming a writer opened the door to movies. I've read thousands of books and there are a few of them I've read twice and a mere handful that I have read more than that. However, the one book I constantly read is the Bible.

I find the scriptures to be instructive on several levels. First and foremost, the Bible is the owner's manual for us to understand the life we've been given and how we should live it. Additionally, the scriptures provide inspiration, motivation, historical perspective, and edification. In this book, Lisa Kimrey has used the Bible as a framework to help us all understand self-care. Far too often, we don't value ourselves to the extent that would allow us to believe that we deserve self-care. But once we realize that this life we've been given and everything in it, is a gift, we begin to understand that how we live is the way we show gratitude for that which we've been given.

FOREWORD

Let's say that I gave you a brand-new sports car on your next birthday. It would please me greatly if you enjoyed the car, used the car, and took care of it. On the other hand, if you took the sports-car I gave you for your birthday and simply parked it in your driveway and ignored it, it would not honor me or the gift that I gave you. In much the same way, but to a far greater extent, the life we have been given is a gift, and we honor our Creator when we enjoy our life and use it to serve others and make the world a better place.

In corporate America, we have unfortunately slipped into the horrible habit of viewing people and treating them as disposable servants of the corporate interest. People are applauded for working late and ignoring weekends, holidays, and vacations. In many of the Asian nations, a culture of honoring workers and the contributions they make to the corporation and its customers has developed. In these organizations, if an individual works late or skips their vacation, they will likely be reprimanded just as if they weren't maintaining a piece of equipment or a corporate vehicle.

I have flown well over two million miles with American Airlines, so I feel like I could give the flight attendants pre-flight speech word for word. Among many other directives, flight attendants explain that if supplemental oxygen is needed, masks will drop down from a compartment above your seat. Then they explain that all passengers should put on their own masks even before they help elderly passengers or even their children to put on their masks. While this might initially seem selfish, the wisdom in these instructions is that if you don't take care of yourself, you'll never be able to take care of anyone else.

Within these pages, you will take a journey with Lisa and learn how to change the world and everything around you as you, first and foremost, learn how to take care of yourself. – Jim Stovall, best-selling author. March 2020

Prologue

Never say you have a dumb question. I once asked God what I thought was the dumbest question ever. You know, those dumb, crazy questions that interrupt your prayer time like how a small child interrupts a parent talking to another adult on the phone? Yeah, it was like that.

But it turns out, it wasn't a dumb question. My question led to *years* of the best conversations I've ever had with God. It led me to insightful and meaningful Scripture. It led me to my life's work and purpose.

And now, it's led me to you!

This book is a summary of the best conversations I've had with the Lord; well, mostly the best lessons about self-care that I've learned from Scripture. I had to share them. You see, I just couldn't keep all of this to myself.

Because once I finally realized where to find the motivation to do my self-care, I knew it would motivate you too.

Introduction

What do you think God eats for breakfast? Eggs and sausage, toast, fruit, and milk? A veggie omelet? A big, delicious jelly donut? I also wonder how God takes care of Himself.

Yes, I'm being a little facetious, but honestly, I think this would be a fascinating discussion to have with the Lord! Why? Because, somewhere in that interesting conversation, God would probably turn the tables by asking us a question.

A life-changing question. Something like:
"What do you think I want YOU to eat for breakfast?" Or maybe:
"How do you think I want YOU to take care of yourself?"

And then, maybe like me, you would stand there a little stunned and just a tad remorseful thinking about what you ate for breakfast, or maybe even your recent personal self-care decisions.

What if that conversation actually happened?

Well, it did in a way. First of all, that's the crazy question I asked during my prayer time a long time ago, "God what do you eat for breakfast?" And secondly, God led me to the place in the Bible where

He tells us there is a connection between *our* self-care and *His* kingdom growth.

What's the connection? God's love and grace.

You see, that's the message I found when I dug into the book of Romans. I learned that taking care of ourselves in an honoring way is another way to worship God, just like singing worship songs, spending time in prayer, and going to church.

But hold on, wait a minute; I'm getting ahead of myself here. For those of you who do not know me, my name is Lisa Kimrey and I am the founder of MyLifeNurse.com. I help you care for your life as you serve and care for others. The idea for this website (and this book!) came out of my journey of learning how to take better care of myself.

What's my journey? Well, a few years ago, I was working as a disease management nurse. One of my roles was to help people make lifestyle changes so they could better manage their chronic diseases (like high blood pressure, diabetes, depression, anxiety, asthma, COPD, heart disease, high cholesterol, etc.). I knew and shared *a lot* of lifestyle improvement knowledge, and I helped a lot of people. But – behind the scenes – I was living off of diet soda and candy-coated peanuts!

Oh, and you've probably heard of the 'can-do kid'? At that time in my life, I was the 'can't stop kid.' I <u>never</u> took the time to take care of myself. NEVER! Why? Well, because honestly, **I thought self-care was a sign of weakness, a sign of vanity, and quite frankly...unnecessary at my age.** (Psst...I basically thought self-care was just for old people!)

Fast forward a few years, and I'm juggling a stressful job and taking care of a baby (that I waited for seven years to arrive) who had colic for nine long months. But I was still not taking good care of myself. Instead, I was working over 50 hours a week while taking care of my family and going on very little sleep, some nights just three hours, one hour at a time. I was still that 'can't stop kid,' but I didn't want to be. I was miserable! I didn't feel well (and was dealing with a rising cholesterol level). I had zero energy, zero creativity, and man, was I cranky! But, as desperate as I was to try to take better care of myself, **I was convinced that I didn't have the time.**

Then, thank God, just a few short months later, I became a stay-at-home mom. A mom who expected life at home to be joyful, peaceful, restful and quiet, who learned that life alone all day with a cranky baby who didn't sleep, wasn't the way the women's magazines depicted it. I was lonely, I was secretly grieving and angry over leaving my lucrative job to stay home 'for this,' and I felt horrible. I was at least 15 pounds heavier, getting more and more depressed every day; I was way under-stimulated, and I realized the only friends I had were all at work. I wasn't the 'can't stop kid' anymore, but at that point, I didn't care because **I was convinced, I wasn't worthy of self-care. Plus, I didn't have <u>any</u> motivation to take better care of myself even if I found my self-worth.**

But, in another way that I couldn't even articulate, I felt called to take better care of myself and do more for the Lord. Unfortunately, I couldn't even begin dreaming about how to serve more. I couldn't even figure out how to eat a healthy breakfast – that's when I asked God what He was having!

So, out of sheer loneliness, and the need to see other adult faces (not because I wanted to or like exercise), I started going to the fitness center which was less than half a mile from our house. I started running around the indoor track just for something to do for 30 minutes (that's desperate, isn't it?). I didn't know how to use the machines (I was too embarrassed to ask) and I didn't feel coordinated enough for the treadmills. So, I started prayer-talking to God when I ran. I prayed that the Lord would give me a passion. Any passion. Just something! I ran and ran. I ran like Forrest Gump! It went on for months.

But God took up my question!

One day while I was running, I was led to a specific verse in the Bible. I wasn't a big reader of Scripture at that time and I had never read the entire Bible, so to have a specific set of verses in my head was quite a surprise, to say the least. Honestly, I thought maybe I was hypoxic from all of the running! I looked up the verses when I got home and felt this incredible burden to learn more. I then spent about a year and a half studying only Romans 12:1-5.

I wrote out my conversations and prayers with God. I wrote out the steps I took, the places I went, and the conversations I had with other people. And I wrote out what I learned in my Scripture study.

What I learned changed my life. Now, I'm hoping it will change yours. Because by the time you finish reading this book I want you to know:

1. What self-care really is.

2. How to tap into the most powerful source of motivation available so you *want* to do self-care (and the source is just waiting for you)!

3. How to make self-care a priority and how to **easily find the time** to do it!

4. How to see your true self-worth so you can give yourself permission to do self-care whenever it's needed.

5. How to use your self-care to live out your God-given purpose and use your gifts to your fullest ability.

6. How to overcome self-care related temptations.

7. How to serve your church and community throughout your entire lifespan (no matter your health status or who else you are caring for or serving).

8. How to avoid burnout while serving the Lord.

Friend, you have been called to do amazing things for the Lord! And worship is one of them. But the thing I suspect you've never thought of is your self-care can be a method to honor or *worship* the Lord. And I bet you have never, ever considered that the everyday minutiae, like how you take care of your body in the morning or night, is pleasing to God.

But it is.

Why is it pleasing to God?

Simply because of the reason you do it. Obedience. Worship.

Shouldn't this be at least a little intriguing to us? As a nurse, I know that **so many of us struggle with our self-care** -- with or without illness. And yet, it pleases God when we offer our bodies or take care of our bodies *with the intent to glorify Him!*

I call this form of obedience and worship 'faith-driven self-care.'

You see, our obedience, or allowing our faith to drive our self-care is freeing. It frees us from the stress of expectations in this world. It frees us from our daily pressures. And it frees us from unnecessary busywork we've been conditioned to think we need to do to take care of ourselves.

But, even more, something vital occurs when we focus on the Lord and worship God with our self-care. It prepares and strengthens our minds and bodies to carry out the Great Commission.

Faith-driven self-care honors the Lord. It makes us well, frees up our schedules, strengthens our self-worth, provides us with motivation, helps us overcome temptations, lends to a healthy and united church, *and* prepares us to grow the Lord's kingdom.

Why *wouldn't* we do this?

Because not many of us know about faith-driven self-care.

So let's get started and unveil this secret!

Chapter 1

The Reset

Once while we were staying at a hotel on the plaza in Kansas City, my husband noticed a tour bus parked in the alley. The name on the side of the bus was out of view, so he cranked his neck and pressed his face against the hallway window. Within seconds he sprung back around, "Hey, I think the Eagles are staying here!"

I went into 'full director mode' and instructed my husband to be ready to get pictures (this was before smartphones, Facebook and Insta) so people would believe we were able to talk to the Eagles (because they'd be walking through the public hallways, right?).

At that moment my husband looked at me and asked a pivotal question. "Lisa, can you name a single song they sing?" Well, as you can probably predict, no, I didn't know, and couldn't even guess the title of a single song. Nor could I claim any of the titles of their album covers or the band members' names.

And, you can probably imagine that my husband knew all of the above.

As a teenager, he had listened to their songs, read stories about band members' lives and careers in magazines, and owned several of their albums or cassettes. He enjoyed listening to their music; he had invested his time and energy in learning all about them and therefore knew every encompassing fact about them. For example, he knew when they wrote the songs, what the words of the songs meant, and why they even wrote the songs in the first place. I had contributed pretty much nothing and only knew *of* them. Our personal investment was the dichotomy of our 'Eagles experience.'

I saw it as a fleeting moment of 'Hey, cool.' My husband experienced a 'WOW moment.' The chance occurrence of seeing the members of the Eagles was a thrilling experience, even though the 'experience' turned out to be *just to see* their tour bus that one time!

'WOW moments' are the moments that make life fun, enjoyable and memorable, aren't they? Those are the events we never forget, and the stories we tell again and again. They leave a footprint in our life journey. In a way, they're also life changing.

This book is about learning how to have a 'WOW moment' experience through your self-care. That means when you finish reading this book, you can have a 'WOW moment' experience *every day*.

I'm sure that seems pretty nutty – that I think taking better care of myself makes my life more enjoyable?

But I do.

And let me tell you I was the biggest skeptic but, now I have a different story. My self-care – and my life – have been changed! And, I believe this is such an amazing 'WOW experience' that I want to help you change your life, too.

So, let's talk about self-care!

What is self-care?

When people are asked the question, "What is self-care?" there're a variety of answers. The great majority of them tend to focus on *actions*.

For example, patients will name specific self-care tasks, maybe what they've always done, or even something based on 'what's trending' or popular in culture. They might tell me what their healthcare provider has told them to do to manage their illness or disease. And sometimes patients will tell me their best tips to treat their stresses of the day.

The other focus is on *the reason* to do it. Many say, "It's what we do to take care of ourselves." Some people even tell me that it's a requirement and they know they need to do it but they don't (which is interesting because it's the people who are struggling to do it who tell me that it's mandatory).

You'd probably agree with me that there isn't anything new or especially interesting in *those* responses.

However, every once in a while, a couple of patients (and I'm talking just one or two people out of a hundred) would say something like, "Self-care is the thing we need to do to take care of our bodies, so we don't struggle. But that's the way God made us."

I'm not going to lie. When I first started asking this question and hearing these few people answer, "That's the way God made us," I wasn't on my 'Christian walk' as churchy people call it. In fact, I usually thought it was an awkward thing to hear, and I would think something like, "Wow, okay, good to know, moving on."

I wasn't reading Scripture at the time. But even now that I am on my 'Christian walk,' I know most of us still wouldn't say that. We don't focus on the big picture or high-level (and I mean super high-level – *kingdom business)* of what self-care is.

And that's when the dichotomy occurs. Most of us know *of* God's kingdom, but the majority of us haven't personally invested time in learning how to answer the question "What is self-care?" in relation to God's kingdom. But when I did look at God's kingdom in scripture to answer the question "What is self-care?" (because of my 'moment' with God which led me to research scripture), I discovered something *amazing.*

Our self-care matters to God. It really does. In fact, it's more important to God than it is to any of us.

Why?

Because our self-care can be a form of worship to God.

Our self-care matters to Him!

You see, many of us know *of* God and agree that He is our Creator, but just like my Eagles story, we haven't invested time in learning more. But when we do, we learn the who, what, when, where, why, how of self-care *related to the Lord's kingdom* (all of which are found in Scripture). We learn that our self-care can be an intimate way to worship God.

So, to sum up, because this is the way God created us, our self-care isn't just for our wellness. Our self-care is also about how to worship God, how we can best serve Him, and how best to carry out our mission, the Great Commission.

Our self-care doesn't just have a personal impact; it also has an eternal impact!

But don't worry about your time or your to-do list. Instead, be encouraged.

You don't need more time to take better care of yourself. You just need to be spiritually present in the time you spend doing your self-care. When you do, all of your systems will flourish and thrive in the way God desires. And, when you thrive the way God desires, kingdom growth will thrive, too!

Follow me as I look at this topic more closely over 5 days.

Why to Offer Your Body

DAY 1

Get Off the Hamster Wheel

I bet I know what you're thinking, "This concept of being spiritually present is great 'biblically.' But, I don't see how this is going to make my life any easier. In fact, it sounds complicated. How is it going to benefit me in my real life?"

Yes, I know. It feels like Scripture tells us about a lot of things that God says are good for us. And, if you're like me, you'd *want* to do them. But, you're not in church every day, and you already have an ongoing battle for the five-minutes of quiet time in the morning. You're managing your home, your on-the-go family, your busy job, the things that fill your day. And, you're probably taking care of or serving other people, too. In fact, serving or taking care of others is likely one of the top reasons you struggle with your self-care and why you are reading this book!

You don't have the time to add one more thing. I get it. But it's worth it! So, let's address that issue first to make sure you don't miss out on something life changing.

I have to ask you to hang in with me here. Because 'getting this' is foundational to you seeing **what's in it for you.**

To start, we need to figure out the real goal here. Is it to be healthy? Is it for wellness? Or is there even a difference? Absolutely yes, there's a difference! Although I hear people use the words *healthy* and *wellness* interchangeably, they are indeed two different things.

In fact, you can have wellness, even when you are in the poorest of health.

Let's examine the definitions of these words for just a minute.

Dictionary.com defines the word **health** as *the general condition of the body or mind with reference to soundness and vigor.*[1] The dictionary goes on to define the word **wellness** as *the quality or state of being healthy in body and mind*, especially *as the result of a deliberate effort.*[2] Think of it this way: consider health as the goal, and wellness as the activity to meet the goal. The activity, or deliberate efforts that people make to improve wellness, are typically through lifestyle changes that target their diet, stress, and exercise. They may even make an effort to change their attitude.

But I want to highlight a Scripture verse that leads us down a totally different path. A better path. A calmer, not the 'hamster wheel' path.

> *Therefore, I urge you, brothers and sisters, in view of God's mercy, to offer your bodies as a living sacrifice, holy and pleasing to God--this is your true and proper worship* (Romans 12:1).

I believe God uses this verse to instruct us to target our activity or deliberate efforts for wellness towards our spiritual worship. Why do I think God asks us to do this? And, more importantly, why should you be obedient to God's request or, in the most basic of terms, why should you change how you think and care for your body?

Because, when we follow God's request and offer our bodies as a living sacrifice, our self-care is included![3] Therefore, you will benefit in at least these three ways:

First, you can better cope with the stress of self-care.

When you focus your wellness efforts on your relationship with God, wellness can become a feeling of peace, comfort, and joy for you in *any state of health.*[4] You can see and feel God's power in the totality of your life; even in the mundane minutiae like how you take care of yourself in the morning or evening, what you eat for lunch, or when you go for a simple walk.

Again, offering your body as a living sacrifice allows you to experience God in the private and difficult area of your suffering – even your seemingly small struggle of taking care of yourself. When the ownership and activity of your self-care is submitted as a form of worship to God, the burden or responsibility of self-care becomes a blessing or source of respite to you. Why? Because your self-care becomes something larger than a thing you just do for yourself. In fact, it's no longer about what you do, but for whom the activity is done.

Need an example? Offering my body as a living sacrifice helped me overcome emotional eating. With not a great deal of activity or effort, over time, I saw that turning to God provided more comfort than eating the candy. This offering (or my submission) also changed how I experienced going to the gym. Something I dreaded (exercise) became something I craved. The transformation was huge for me. I believed I was someone who needed candy/sugar to cope. I believed I hated to exercise. Years later, I still live a transformed life. And, through both transformations, I have felt peace and calm.

The peace of the spiritual connection eclipses the distress of doing self-care. In other words, you can better cope with the stress of 'doing the self-care' because you don't have to actively make self-care a priority when you casually desire the calm of this freedom.

Secondly, you can get off the hamster wheel.

I hope I've established how this form of worship puts your focus on God. When you focus on God, you turn your focus away from yourself. But there's more. You can also turn your focus away from the exhausting cultural trends, and even human notions or activities of wellness. In other words, you get out of the hamster wheel. Our increasing desires for health and wellness has created a profitable industry. Everyone wants to tell you the best superfood or diet, exercise, stress reliever, meditation method, medication, or natural remedy for ultimate wellness. Deciphering it all is completely overwhelming. So what do we think? "Why stick with one – let's join the rat race of self-care and pursue them all!"

Unfortunately, well-written marketing media and sales copy is so convincing that many of us, myself included, will jump on the self-care hamster wheel without:

- Researching if it has any scientific validity.
- Assessing whether the pursuit is truly needed.

- Considering how much commitment is required to do the activities.
- Reflecting about this in prayer.

Ever wonder what drives us to this hamster wheel? What's the motivator? Do you know, the deep desire or the energy source the advertisers are tapping into and using to push so many of us into this rat race? I believe it's nothing more than FOMO. Fear Of Missing Out. The fear of missing out is driving us to try to do everything. We want to do *all-of-the-things*. Unfortunately, this is an exhausting energy source – and, remember, fear doesn't come from the Lord.

Romans 12:1 has a source of energy. Your faith, discipline, and obedience to God is the energy that drives your desire to worship, honor and please Him. In other words: through faith, you have access to a helpful, and motivating source of energy. As an added bonus, you tap into the power of the Holy Spirit which saves *your* mental and emotional energy.

But the key point here is that this isn't a big list of new things to learn or do to take better care of yourself. It's doing ONE thing that you are somewhat already familiar with: worship, to gain access to the Ultimate Power Source.

Finally, you actively live out your faith.

Isn't it amazing that all of the above can occur when you place your focus on God instead of yourself? It's a literal way to actively live out your faith, and you can experience the *goodness* of humble obedience.

When you offer your body as a living sacrifice, you are taking an obedient *action* towards becoming a mission-capable soldier for God.

<u>This process prepares your mind and body for the Great Commission!</u> Obedience to God is the catalyst to seeing other people's needs (instead of just your own). After you see the needs of others, you see the value of serving others.[5] It helps **you see how to bring glory to God through every part of your life.**

And, in response to our obedience, God will deliver on His promises of wellness that are listed throughout scripture. The promises include assisting us with our everyday needs of survival, wisdom, guidance, comfort, strength, protection and, even at times, healing. We will go through a few of these promises throughout the study.

Friend, I've been praying for you. My hope is that you decide to walk forward with me.

Let's get started. Please do this Quick Workout to assess your need for peace.

QUICK WORKOUT: PLEASE THINK ABOUT AND ANSWER THE QUESTIONS BELOW.

The peace of our spiritual connection to God far outweighs the distress of doing our self-care, (and perhaps even our physical or mental/emotional symptoms or our illness).

In what areas of your life do you need God's peace?

Please check any of the boxes that apply to you. There could be more than one.

WHERE I NEED PEACE						
Nutritional intake	☐	Fitness	☐	Family/ Relationships	☐
Professional & Creative Learning	☐	Finances	☐	Safety & Security	☐
Social & Friend Network	☐	Preventive Healthcare	☐	Illness Care & Treatment	☐
Spirituality	☐	Thought Life	☐	Expressing & Processing Emotions	☐

Anything else? _____

How many did you check? There is no right or wrong answer.
If you marked more than three, then peace is an issue. Please read on because you will find the answer.

Let's pray. Father, I come to You because I need Your peace in all these areas of my life (name them). All this while I have been striving to work things out on my own. But now I ask You to take control of them all and help me make the right choices. Holy Spirit, I now ask for Your peace to envelope me and I cast my burdens on to You.

DAY 2

Align Your Priorities

Do you remember The Exodus? It's one of my favorite books in the Old Testament and it's about how God led the Israelites out of Egypt to escape Pharaoh's bondage. On this fascinating journey, the Israelites saw miracles and experienced God's presence through their adventure and awe, and through their faith and obedience. Morale was high, and their allegiance was strong! And then…they were in the wilderness!

After only a short time, the stress and responsibility of their freedom were so high that slavery began to look like paradise. They whined and complained about the monotonous diet and their physical discomforts. The more they whined, the less trust and faith they exhibited. But God never left them. He provided wisdom and guidance to Moses as well as manna, water, and quail to the people. Even though the Israelites were rarely grateful, God still provided everything they needed; from daily bread to knowledge, protection, comfort, and healing.

In Exodus, God wanted to do all of the leading and all of the work, and He wanted the people to just trust and obey Him. If you read Exodus 14-16, you will find that God was in front of, alongside, or behind the people performing miracles based on His plan. In fact, God gives instructions and a promise, showing how their obedience would result in wellness. *"If you listen carefully to the Lord your God and do what is right in his eyes, if you pay attention to his commands and keep all of his decrees, I will not bring on you any of the diseases I brought on the Egyptians, for I am the Lord, who heals you"* (Exodus 15:26).

Do you see how God wanted to be their focus, and then offered a promise of wellness if He was?

By looking deeper into the Exodus story, you will see that they witnessed both a real and a spiritual freedom from bondage. They experienced real freedom because they were no longer Pharaoh's slaves. But they also experienced spiritual freedom because God was always with them. They were free from the ways of the Egyptian culture; thus, they were spared from sickness in spite of the harsh conditions. All through that journey God guided them through their leader Moses, and all their basic needs were met. Along the way they sinned many times, even rebelled. God dealt with such rebellion but, when they repented, He was quick to pardon them. By the time they made it to the Promised Land they were set free in many aspects of their lives.

He was their first priority.

During all of this, He made Himself their priority. The manna, water, and quail were not just the means of survival in the wilderness. These things represent God's sustenance – His care for them; provision, guidance, comfort, and protection. It was His way of showing His presence in their lives at their point of need. Even in their disobedience, they knew they had to depend on Him for their continued survival.

This Old Testament story shows us what God can do when He becomes our priority. We see how God wanted the Israelites to trust Him, and as they did, His people were well, united and victorious over their enemies. God provided their basic needs, but He also saved them from the curses of Egypt. At the same time, He is glorified!

Today, offering your body as a living sacrifice places faith in God as the first priority of your life. God wants you to trust and depend on Him above all things. And, when you decide to worship God with your body (and self-care), your faith will be strengthened. Your trust and dependence on God will deepen through your discipline and obedience. In return, you are freed from the bondage of the trendy wellness solutions in our culture.

QUICK WORKOUT: PLEASE THINK ABOUT AND ANSWER THE QUESTIONS BELOW.

How will making God your first priority change your life?

A lot	☐
Somewhat	☐
Not much	☐
Not sure	☐

Place a checkmark by the things in the list below that you are currently prioritizing before God?

Entertainment	☐
Hobbies	☐
Work & Chores	☐
Travel	☐
Relationships	☐

Social media ☐

Exercise & Fitness ☐

Study ☐

Anything else? _____

Will you agree with me?

Let's pray together. Lord, I realize that I have put a lot of things ahead of You. Please forgive me. To receive Your peace, give me the resolve to make You my number one priority, in Jesus' name.

DAY 3

Make Better Choices

The Exodus example is not the only place in the Old Testament where we can see that obedience to God brings wellness. The Bible is rich in examples.

Another topic that I want to discuss is when and why the Israelites made atonement sacrifices. I've highlighted a couple of biblical points that spoke to me and helped me see why it is so important to understand the significance of the atonement and to be obedient to God's instructions in my life. I hope these points help you, too.

God's Ways Are Good

Ceremonial sacrifices represented a way for the Israelites to either worship God or restore their right standing with Him. They were governed by an enormous number of specific rules and guidelines (as in the book of Leviticus). From the outside, they looked extremely ritualistic. But today, when we look at the descriptions of some of the laws and sacrifices, we can see that they also describe – in very basic terms – safe ways to take care of themselves. For example, food safety, disease and illness prevention, proper hygiene, infection control, and healing.

The entire process kept them clean or holy for God. It contributed to their wellness, and in many cases, kept them alive. At base they *knew with certainty* that the laws were relevant to their relationship with God and that through them they would experience worship, atonement, and spiritual cleansing. However, they probably didn't realize that these laws were safe self-care steps as well, and many times, they also experienced physical and emotional or mental cleansing through them.

We Thrive When We Follow God

The Israelites were never able to keep all of the laws. And because they couldn't be restored without atonement, animal sacrifice was an *all-consuming process* for them to stay 'clean.' Their obedience to His laws honored Him and then drove them to choices that were beneficial and made them well. We often miss it, but that was the whole point; God wants us to see how much we need Him. We need God continuously to thrive—even in today's ready-made culture!

Acknowledge God's Grace

Multiple theologians call the Old Testament atonement process a 'taking' (death) form of sacrifice because the offerings required the killing of unblemished animals. All these sacrifices point us to Jesus Christ, who served as our ultimate and final 'taking' sacrifice at the crucifixion. Paul, in the book of Romans, wants us to see the crucifixion and resurrection of Jesus as the apex of spiritual freedom bringing about our salvation. That's where we can see God's profound *agape* (or unconditional) love in our relationship with the Father, Christ, and the Holy Spirit.

Paul wrote Romans 12 after writing 9 chapters describing the deep ugliness of our sin, how we cannot save ourselves, and how we do not deserve forgiveness. Then in Chapter 10, he describes how we can be saved through God's forgiving grace when we repent of our sins and believe in the death and resurrection of His Son, Jesus. Paul wants us to understand that God is merciful and compassionate, but our forgiveness came at a steep price; God sacrificed His beloved Son <u>for us</u>. We **cannot** save ourselves or repay the debt.

Paul went on to write Chapter 12 to say <u>because of the grace we receive from God, we should be in awe.</u> In other words, acknowledge with admiration and with honor such an amazing solution.

Simply put, we should worship God!

We Honor God with Obedience

Therefore, Paul encourages us to be obedient to God with our bodies, that is to say, worship God in every aspect of our lives. Let it become the new standard of how we use and take care of our bodies. To go even deeper, Paul uses Romans 12:1 to tell Christians to move towards a 'giving' kind of sacrifice as a way to honor and praise God. Thus, we shouldn't take care of ourselves just to be healthy or well. Rather, we should do so as a way to <u>honor</u> God.

He IS the moral authority.

He IS God!

He is the *ultimate* moral authority and IS the active power to transform human life according to His divine intention.

HE CAN change your life!

We have a great example of what a giving sacrifice looks like: Jesus. **Jesus served not only as the ultimate 'taking' sacrifice, but as the ultimate 'giving' sacrifice!**

When we choose to give our bodies *as a living sacrifice*, our actions glorify God.[6] When we offer or give our bodies as a sacrifice to God to honor and worship Him, the decisions and submission, our actions, and our deliberate acts of will become an offering, which *is holy and pleasing to God*. We must come to God believing that we have been made holy by the blood, putting on Christ's breastplate of righteousness. Any other form of holiness would be through works (Ephesians 2:10).

Self-care, when done as a giving sacrifice, therefore, becomes a way of spiritual worship versus just ordinary, worldly self-care.

Make Better Choices

What an honor it is for us to serve in this manner! As Christ's followers, it truly is our privilege to worship such a loving God. As we realize more and more that self-care is really about God, (and not about us) <u>our desires will change</u>.

Paul's phrase, 'to offer your bodies,' is a reference and tie-back to those Old Testament sacrifices, which represented the totality of their lives and activities.[7] When we offer our bodies to God today, we can bring Him into the totality of our lives, too. Our respect and adoration for God drives us to obedience, thus changing our desires and **driving us to make better choices for our own bodies.**

QUICK WORKOUT: PLEASE THINK ABOUT AND ANSWER THE QUESTIONS BELOW.

How do you think acknowledging God's grace would improve or change your self-care? Tick the answers that you agree with.

☐ I see now that self-care pleases Him because I am honoring Him with my body.

☐ Honoring Him with my body is a form of worship.

☐ My body is His temple and it is holy. Therefore, I should take care of it.

☐ Self-care that puts the focus on God brings peace.

How many of these statements do you agree with? If you agree with ALL of them you are on the right track.

What happens when your self-care operates from your own self-interest and methods?

_____

_____

_____

Now, spend a few moments in prayer.

DAY 4

Get Powerful Motivation!

There are times when worship and obedience will require discipline. Discipline is built and strengthened by intentional thoughts and actions. How often have you read the word 'intentional' in faith-based media lately? I see it used in blogs, websites, news stories, and books showing how to be intentional while raising our children, approaching our marriage, managing our finances, services, and businesses, and I've even seen 'intentional' in grocery shopping.

However, the word is used less frequently in Christian literature. As Christians, let's be intentional not only in prayer but in all our pursuits.

We can get a feel for how intentional Christians are with their self-care by looking at health outcomes. For example:

- Northwestern University performed a study in 2011 which tracked 3,433 men and women for 18 years and reported that those who attended church or a bible study once a week were 50% more likely to be obese.[8]
- A 2006 Purdue study found that fundamental Christians are by far the heaviest of all religious groups, led by the Baptists with a 30% obesity rate. Jews compare at 1%, and Buddhists and Hindus are at 0.7%.[9]
- In 2001, a Pulpit and Pew study of 2,500 clergies reported that 76% were overweight or obese compared to the general population at the time of the survey.[10]

Allowing for some overgeneralization, these statistics show that people of faith do have at least *a little* room to be more intentional with their self-care thoughts and actions. In fact, for most of us, our worst habits hit us the hardest somehow related to our self-care. Think about it. How many of us get up every morning with great intentions, only to start a routine that accommodates our busy, over-packed and stressful schedules and convenience needs?

Most of our daily decisions reflect our own concoctions to satisfy our personal desires, which have become automatic responses to please *ourselves* (our bad habits!). For the most part, we know the things we *should* do as good self-care, but we just *don't want to do*. Why is that?

Well, my surveys (and my own experiences) tell me that we:

- Don't make them a priority.
- Say we don't have the time.
- Lack the motivation.
- Don't think we know how to do self-care correctly.

We also try to make excuses saying that the amount we need to learn and the size of our lifestyle changes have to be huge. In fact, this isn't true – small changes work! Furthermore, our self-care flaws (i.e. bad habits) – the ones that hurt our health and wellness – aren't even a secret to us. We know they include poor food choices, unmanaged stress, little or no exercise, and little or no time spent with God, among other things. Typically, we're not at all surprised with this list or its effect on our physical, emotional and mental stability. And, we're not surprised that we fail at changing.

But we sure like to talk about the intentional talk.

Have you ever noticed the big fanfare when we decide we are going to make a 'change' in our habits? We practically sound trumpets when we put our intentions on social media, buy new special 'work-out' clothes, maybe splurge on equipment or memberships, buy special food or supplements, commit to giving more energy and time, join up with friends, and so on.

It's go big or go home, right?

The list is endless really. But two things stand out for me as a symbol of our enormous efforts: the short-term buzz, and the predictable failure to change our habits.

New Year's Resolutions

What have you said on New Year's Eve? I know what I've said:

- I'm finally going to eat right and get healthy!
- I'm going to go to church regularly!
- I'm setting my priorities straight!

We go at it with big preparatory words and actions, vast life-changing goals, and huge commitments. A few achieve, but so, so many *never get past the first week*. It's so true that helping people meet their own goals is a booming business! We talk about the intentional talk, but we sure don't walk the intentional walk.

Where then DO we turn to strengthen our intentions to take better care of ourselves?

Well, we sure know where it's not.

It's not in big aspirations and glam
It's not in loud efforts
It's not in the latest trend or in culture

It's no to all! We achieve it through a decision to offer our body to God, and then look to the Lord for strength with every decision related to our self-care.

Our intentions are strengthened in the quiet faithfulness of the Lord. And, the Lord helps us use our intentions to build and strengthen the discipline of self-control.

When we are faithful to worship and praise God with our self-care, we experience spiritual growth. We begin to have a connection with God that can only occur through faithfulness. Our self-control is strengthened. And we are given the *desire* to be obedient.

The desire to please God provides the _motivation_ to perform the self-care actions that bring glory to God.

The strength and power of the Holy Spirit improves your self-care because:

- There is unlimited power in self-control from the Holy Spirit compared to the limited willpower of our human efforts. Self-control is, after all, of the fruit of the Holy Spirit.
- There is an ease of effort from the faithful performance of the Holy Spirit compared to the striving required of our human efforts to meet our commitments.

- There is calm in the presence of the Holy Spirit's peace compared to the loud frenzy to fulfill our worldly desires.

We don't achieve this with fanfare. We achieve it on a quiet journey with the Lord.

We each have unique bodies. So we will each have a unique experience as we use our bodies and minds to worship the Lord. For example, living as a holy sacrifice may reveal how to:

1. Break free of 'fleshly bonds,' i.e. cravings, wants, or poor self-care habits.
2. Identify your spiritual gift(s) and call for service.
3. Discover wellness, or sickness prevention, to allow for a future or life-long service for the Lord.
4. Share your experience of suffering to provide hope to others experiencing the same.
5. Serve as a living image of grace and dignity while facing a challenging illness or possibly death.
6. Learn that the change may have little or no effect on the physical body or your mind or emotions, but an inward change to the soul.
7. Develop a more intimate relationship with Christ.

Amazingly, although each of us will be strengthened and grow individually, the Lord's kingdom grows through the strengthened obedience of us all.

Friend, we can find great joy through our basic self-care. We can worship God, experience the awesomeness of the Holy Spirit and have the opportunity to see God work in our daily lives. The fruit of the

Holy Spirit is available to provide self-control, faithfulness, and peace in your self-care efforts. In fact, it is available to you right now. You do not have to wait for a major symptom or illness to happen. Paul's words encourage us to think a little differently. We can pray and ask God for help with our self-care, or with a minor symptom *before* an advanced diagnosis comes.

QUICK WORKOUT: PLEASE THINK ABOUT AND ANSWER THE QUESTIONS BELOW.

What excites you most about the help of the Holy Spirit in your self-care efforts?
- ☐ Self-control
- ☐ Faithfulness
- ☐ Peace
- ☐ All of the above

Could you explain why?

_____

_____

_____

Let's pray together. Lord, I don't know what my experience will be like as I start to live as a holy sacrifice, but I know you already know. I am excited and look forward to growing stronger spiritually as I become closer to you on this journey.

DAY 5

Experience Less Stress

I'm sure the statement, "our bodies are not maintenance free," isn't a surprise to anyone because most of us view our upkeep to be quite an arduous task! But we're *busy* – an understatement for many of us. That's why, when we are not intentionally seeking the quiet faithfulness of God, it is so, so tempting to choose the 'easy-button', the shortcut, or the path of least resistance to self-care.

Whatever it looks like in your life, there's something you should know._All_ of the above interfere with kingdom growth because they put our focus on ourselves and not the Lord.

Although Christians are typically not intentional about worshiping God with our self-care, the distractions towards ungodly self-care efforts *are* intentional.

This is no accident.

Our enemy <u>benefits</u> when we put our energy into trendy and cultural methods to improve our lifestyles and change our habits. Why does our enemy profit? Because when we place our efforts on culturally based self-care or self-improvement, **we feel stress**. And when we feel stressed, we focus on...ourselves.

No longer is self-care about rest and recharge in our culture. It's another form of pressure to look perfect. We've allowed self-care to be turned into a commodity. It's become synonymous with a long list of expectations and tasks that we keep adding to when we learn new things from product and service marketing and a multitude of unscientific sources.

Need an example? The peer-pressure is so prevalent we see memes about it on our social media feeds! In fact, there's one particular meme I will never forget. It contains an image of a stressed mom who is trying to get her kids to school somewhere. She's frantically rushing her kids out the door all the while thinking:

Did I drink eight cups of water? I need to sign up for yoga soon. And Pilates. Thank goodness I had time to make Susie the bento box of cutely carved fruits and veggies I saw on Pinterest. I need to pick up more of the non-GMO veggie sticks. I wish I could find more ways to recycle. Oh, I haven't taken my 14 supplements yet. I'll take them with lunch. Oops, today is my fasting day, I'll just take them later while I'm juicing all of the organic produce I just bought. I need to squeeze in some meditation time before that. Then I'll do that charcoal mask to clarify my skin...

Relatable, right? Sadly, the reason I'll never forget this meme is because of what I saw next on my social media feed. A young mom I know in real life asked on social media how other people were able to achieve all of said self-care tasks because she couldn't do so. She was obviously a hot mess who couldn't get herself together and was feeling bad about herself but probably deserved it because she was behind on self-care.

We've accepted a marketing sham that shifts our focus to ourselves.

When we are focused on ourselves, we miss:

- The blessings God places around us
- God's wisdom
- God's promptings
- Opportunities to be obedient to and serve God
- Opportunities for God to equip us for larger tasks

God created our bodies with a unique design. Our physical, mental and emotional, and spiritual systems are woven into one person who *can* praise and worship Him with our self-care. And the act of worshiping God with our self-care lifts our own burdens and provides the calm consistency that helps us overcome the struggles of taking care of ourselves.

QUICK WORKOUT: PLEASE THINK ABOUT AND ANSWER THE QUESTION BELOW.

When do you find yourself tempted to choose the easy way out in relation to your self-care? Choose all that apply.

□ Too many chores	□ Feel guilty about something
□ Emotionally upset	□ Stressed out or weary
□ Out with friends	□ Tempting snack nearby
□ Trying to concentrate	□ Watching TV or movies
□ Caring for others	□ Overcommitted/no time
□ No self-care goal	□ No self-care plan

Any other occasion?

_____

Let's pray together. Lord, I do not want to focus on myself. When I do, I miss Your blessings, wisdom and promptings. Help me recognize when I am tempted to take the easy way. I want to return my gaze to You and receive Your promises. I want to serve You.

A Promise from God

"But I will restore you to health and heal your wounds,"
says the Lord, "because you are called an outcast, Zion, for
whom no one cares."' (Jeremiah 30:17).

In this particular context, Israel's condition of being an outcast nation appears pretty hopeless. But God promises to heal them and restore them to spiritual health. Then, He intervenes to change the gloomy outlook for them.

At the end of the day, the people realized that *it was God who orchestrated* their outcast status in the first place (and not the surrounding nations). Ultimately, this provided them with the hope they needed at just the right time.

God can change His intentions in response to a change in our attitudes and the way we worship Him. Like the above promise, He promises a genuine, saving solution. God promises complete healing for our sick hearts. God can also heal us physically, mentally, and emotionally to give us wellness, although not always through the 'treatments' we know.

We cannot save ourselves through any good deed, good work, on our own accord of high morals, or by being a good person. The grace of salvation, spending eternity in heaven with Jesus, is available by admitting we are sinners, repenting of our sins, and asking Jesus into our hearts to be our Savior. Jesus is our Savior and Redeemer because

He traded places with us and took our punishment – death for *our* sins – to make us new creations.

When we accept Jesus as our Savior and live our lives for Him, we will certainly look like 'outcasts' of this world. But, remember that we were CREATED TO BE OUTCASTS. What would our obedience with our self-care say to the people in the world? Consider what we could do for Christ if we turned to Him to restore our wellness.

How could YOU **change the world** if you allowed people to see YOU as an outcast?

QUICK WORKOUT: PLEASE THINK ABOUT AND ANSWER THE QUESTION BELOW.

God provided the promise in Jeremiah 30:17 as a reminder that He has set us apart from the rest of the people in the world. He *created* us to be outcasts.

In what ways does knowing you are created to be set apart from the people around you change the way you look at the cultural expectations of self-care? Are you starting to see there is an alternative?

RECAP

Why should you reset your life?

- Get Off My Hamster Wheel
- Align My Priorities
- Make Better Choices
- Get Powerful Motivation!
- Experience Less Stress

Worshiping in this way allows us to experience God in such a close and intimate way that all our systems flourish and thrive.

My challenge to you is to keep reading to learn how to turn your energy and effort away from ineffective cultural prescriptions, and instead intentionally focus your self-care efforts in quiet obedience to a faithful God.

When you do, you will thrive! And when you thrive, kingdom growth thrives!

Chapter 2

Renew Your Thinking

One of my favorite memories with my now 25-year-old son is way back when he was about six or seven-years-old. We were finishing dinner one night, and he excitedly asked, "What's for dessert?" My husband and I knew we had an ice-cold, peak-of-the-season watermelon in the cooler and so we both proudly responded, Watermelon!"

"What?" My son yelled in complete horror, "Fruit for dessert!"

That situation taught me something.

Perspective. Is. *Everything!*

Your perspective is your view of a situation or the way you see things from the lens of whatever is affecting you. It's your outlook, your frame of mind. Therefore, your perspective has power. Perspective can drive your beliefs, attitudes, decisions and, ultimately, your behavior. Having a proper perspective is vital to the success of whatever you're doing. And, if you're like me when you first wake-up, you try to have a good perspective to get a jump start on making that day productive.

Perspective affects our future, too. In fact, it is critical to understand that a major part of changing our future starts by changing our perspective today. And, specific to our well-being, we can impact our future health and wellness outcomes with a *proper* perspective change now.

So how should we do this? What's the best source to find the proper perspective? Well, in Chapter 1 I talked about the value of seeing wellness as part of our spiritual activity. And, I believe the proper source for a perspective change comes from the Lord through worship, scripture, praise, faith, and prayer.

As a registered nurse, I've been a witness to my patients' perspective changes and their improved wellness outcomes. Often, I've seen this occur through the act of prayer. Whether they choose this goal or not, I can't be certain. But what I do know is that, when the patient was praying, *they looked to the Lord to change their perspective.*

The most *powerful* way I've seen people allow the Lord to guide their mindset is to deal with their worry. I've watched hundreds of people replace anxiety and fear with inexplicable peace and calm. In fact, some of the calmest, most peaceful *and joyful* patients I've ever taken care of were actually in the dying process.

As a result of all of this, I've observed a fascinating phenomenon.

Patients, who used faith to change their perspective, coped better *with* the experience, regardless *of* the experience. But I don't think this phenomenon is just a nursing observation -- rather I believe it's one of the finest, real-life examples of how God wants us to *live out* our faith.

Going back to what I said in Chapter 1 about Romans 12:1, offering God our bodies as a form of worship allows us to apply our faith in *every* part of our daily lives. It also provides us the opportunity to change our perspective in *any* of our circumstances.

I remember how my perspective first began to transform:

I was home taking care of my toddler. The fog of fatigue, boredom, and loneliness drove me to drown my sorrows by eating a variety of candy — a lot!

The world's message is 'Treat me.' And, I was doing my darndest to treat myself. I was practically living on candy at the time.

But I was struggling. My mind told me to 'treat myself' one minute, and 'refrain from all treats' the next.

Yes, I wanted to be home with my child, but I felt like I was just sitting there, wasting my education and energy away. How could singing the same songs, playing the same games, doing the same chores day after day after day be what I was supposed to be doing?

I prayed. I always prayed.

But that day I noticed I was angry. Why was this happening over and over and over?

I looked at my candy stash again. An entire cupboard. My very own candy shop.

Where was He? I had prayed so many times asking Him to comfort me, but I felt nothing. I only felt alone. Not worthy of His comfort. Not worthy to take better care of myself. Who would care?

Then I said it. "No," I shouted out loud to God, "Why don't you stop me from eating this candy?"

It was strangely quiet.

And, then it happened.

I heard (an inaudible voice) in my mind say, "I want you to want Me."

This chapter is going to explore Scriptures that teach us how to change our thinking and our perspective. We need to allow God to renew our way of thinking for three vital reasons:

- It teaches us what a proper perspective is according to Him.
- It's the catalyst for a behavior transformation.
- It's an act of obedience.

Let's dive into learning more about why and how to allow God to renew our thinking.

How to Renew Thinking

DAY 1

Allow Transformation to Begin

Have you ever noticed that what we think we see is not always an accurate depiction of its potential?

For example, have you ever looked at an architect's blueprint? To most of us, it's just a rendering, an outline or a sketch of what is to be. When we look at the blueprint, we can't always see the purpose of the construction. But, hidden inside the code of the blueprint, the creator ensures it contains not just the basic framework but also the details of the entire project.

The builder can look at the same basic rendering and see the beautiful product the creator intended in the design. We can't see how the design impacts the character or personality of the structure. But the builder sees what's hidden; they know what treasures are waiting inside that design. The builder instantly recognizes the blueprint's marvelous potential. The structure, character, or personality of the construction has a purpose to the builder – just as it did for the creator.

It's the same with how we see our bodies. God created us. And we have an opportunity to build from what He created. We're the builders, although we may not see the purpose of why we are created a certain way. We may not see the beauty in the way we are designed.

But our bodies have the details, the purpose. Our bodies contain hidden treasures – marvelous potential – set in place by our Creator.

As a result, we must get our minds set in the right context so we can discover *and appreciate* our purpose …and hidden treasures. Ironically, these hidden treasures can so often be the things we don't like about ourselves after they're discovered. Once we can appreciate them, we can then build, or live out, what our God has created in us.

But, how do we change our perspective towards the things that we call our weaknesses, inadequacies, or flaws? In my opinion, there's only one way, and that's letting God reestablish our thinking so we can see ourselves through His eyes, the eyes of our Creator.

Appreciate Our Hidden Treasures

We need to discover who God created us to be and what He created us to do for Him. **Learning our purpose, and also appreciating the value in the hidden treasures as much as God does, is the KEY to changing our perspective regarding our lifestyle.**

Let's look at a scripture verse and then walk through some commentaries for further revelation to explore this topic.

> *Do not conform to the pattern of this world, but be transformed by the renewing of your mind. Then you will be able to test and approve what God's will is—his good, pleasing and perfect will'* (Romans 12:2).

When we allow God to give us a new perspective and transform the way we think, we have an opportunity to learn God's good (His truth).

In Romans 12:2, Paul exhorts that we *"be transformed,"* this is, 'keep on being transformed' by the renewing of our mind. The Greek verb for 'transformed' is the root of the English word 'metamorphosis,' meaning a total change from the inside out. The key to this change is the 'mind,' the control center of our attitudes, thoughts, feelings, and actions. As our mind keeps on being made new by the spiritual input of God's Word, prayer and Christian fellowship, our lifestyle keeps on being transformed.[11]

Have you ever noticed how powerless and weak we feel when we try to change our attitudes or behavior on our own merit? Or how about when we look to our culture for support or assistance? On the other hand, allowing God to renew our thinking gives us a new perspective *and* the power of the Holy Spirit *to help us* take to the next step for change. And taking one step is ALL that we need to do to begin!

Paul did not say change our lives and instantly become a perfect follower. He stated that allowing God to renew our mind is the *beginning* of a continuous and ongoing transformation. Paul adds, "Then we will learn to know God's will for us, which is good and pleasing and perfect." Paul uses the word 'then' to say that after we allow God to renew our thinking, then God will help us learn His plan for us.

God will lead us on a journey to discover our purpose and how to love and use the qualities He gave us. We'll have the opportunity to test out what God wants for us. As we move forward with the new perspective, we will experience God's goodness. We'll know God's will and then learn how to trust His good, pleasing and perfect will in our lives.

These three qualities are not attributes of God's will...rather, God's will itself is what is good, well-pleasing to Him, and perfect. In other words, God's will or intent IS good. God wants us to trust Him, so we experience the goodness He intends for us.[12]

So, it may be a surprise to hear that one of the most common and significant ways we stumble when we start our transformation journey is that we forget about the goodness of God. In fact, sometimes, we narrow our vision and focus only on the laws and standards. "We fall into the mindset that God is trying to put a bunch of rules and regulations in our life. However, by focusing more on His goodness, we realize that God isn't trying to minimize our joy or happiness, but is rather, in fact, trying to maximize it, knowing that His law is for our good and joy in the end."[13]

QUICK WORKOUT: PLEASE THINK ABOUT AND ANSWER THE QUESTION BELOW.

In your self-care you only need to take one step at a time. As you do, you are going to experience a continuous transformation. Explain how knowing this encourages you.

_____

_____

_____

Spend a few minutes in prayer.

DAY 2

Fear God

God created us to look at Him fearfully, or with reverence. One definition of reverence is to look at someone with respect tinged with awe, or an overwhelming feeling of admiration. I think it's natural to feel awe towards God. He is everywhere, He has marvelous knowledge, He created the entire universe. Most importantly, nothing has ever been hidden from God, not today and not even when He uniquely created each of us in our mother's womb.

And then, in darkness, in our struggles, God sees, loves and truly *knows* us, even when we have conflicts within our own minds or bodies. I think that's one reason that God gives us this renewed reflective view – to give us the ability to look at ourselves through *His* eyes whenever we need it. God wants us to know that, although the reasons He designed us in a certain way may not always be clear to *us*, they are always clear to *Him*. There's comfort in knowing that the way God forms us, even the things we don't like about ourselves, were known to Him, with His purpose and function in mind, from the very beginning.

The **purpose** of our creation is explained in God's Word and helps us understand why our self-care affects us not only through physical outcomes but spiritual results as well. Genesis 1:27 reads, *"So God created man in His own image; He created him in the image of God..."* Scripture affirms that we are created in God's image, not in our parents' image.

The word 'image' translates to shadow, or reflection, in the Hebrew language. The Hebrew concept stresses the <u>function</u> of the word, or the way the word operates, not the <u>form.</u> Therefore, when we read that we are created in God's image, it means that God created us with *His* purpose in mind.[14]

Because God tells us that we are created to be a shadow of His service (meaning His goals, purposes, thoughts), He wants us to understand that *our* purpose is to live our lives as a *reflection* of Him in how we act, believe or think. God gave us the Holy Spirit (who resides in our bodies when we accept Jesus as our Lord and Savior) to help us achieve that purpose.

Fearing God or remembering Him with reverence is the proper perspective because He knows our purpose better than we would ever know it ourselves!

QUICK WORKOUT: PLEASE THINK ABOUT AND ANSWER THE QUESTIONS BELOW.

In what ways can you show reverence to God?

_____

_____

_____

Spend a few moments in prayer. Then, name some ways fearing God can lift you up when you are feeling low, unworthy, or unimportant.

_____

_____

_____

Embrace the Fact that We Are Wonderfully Made

While our God is so awesome and powerful in creating all life, He also knows every single detail about us. He not only knows our bodies, but He also knows our thoughts, motivations, unique abilities and our daily routines. The specificity of God's knowledge can be amazing and overwhelming.

As a result, understanding that God created us for His purposes (and not our benefit or pleasure) *can be a motivator* for us to take better care of ourselves. It also helps us to identify our uniqueness and to appreciate how we can serve *God in our exclusive way.* Using faith to embrace that you were formed in God's image and purposely created in a wonderful, beautiful way provides a path to love yourself as God loves you.

Furthermore, your faith helps you accept that your body is indeed used as a spiritual temple when the Holy Spirit dwells in it. Self-care done with the intent of being holy to your body, the temple of the Holy Spirit, honors God.

On the other hand, different things in our culture can interfere with our relationship with God. They make us think we should feel ashamed, hopeless, or embarrassed about areas where we believe we are created as 'less than.' Some of us may even begin to 'hate' our weakness, our bodies, or minds, and be drawn away from God (instead of praising Him) by believing lies like, "God made a mistake on me," or "My eyes are too small." We may even try to hide our negative (lying) feelings about ourselves by finding comfort in worldly provisions (food, drink, shopping, money, sex, drugs, plastic surgery). The reality is that most of us, if not all, have something about our body or mind that we do not like. We may also have traits or attributes that we do not believe are any good.

The world judges our 'flaws' *and* wants us to judge ourselves and hate our 'weaknesses' no matter who created the 'flaw or weakness.' But God wants our praise for everything He created – because *His will* is good! The Bible says we are fearfully and wonderfully made (Psalm 139:20). He provides us comfort in His word and desires that we instead praise and thank Him for how we are formed.

Look at God fearfully and with reverence. The self-care choices we make today matter to God. Our body was designed to be the Holy Spirit's residence. Our body was designed for a purpose. We have a responsibility to build or live out that purpose.

Let's agree.

QUICK WORKOUT: PLEASE THINK ABOUT AND ANSWER THE QUESTIONS BELOW.

List anything in your physical body that you now see as good which you previously saw as a flaw or weakness.

_____

_____

_____

How do you think God will use it?

_____

_____

_____

How can fearing God and embracing that you are wonderfully made be helpful when you tend to neglect taking care of yourself?

_____

_____

_____

Let's pray together. Father, I thank You that I am wonderfully and fearfully made (Psalm 139:20). I praise You that I am created in Your image. Therefore, everything about me is perfect in Your eyes. In the eyes of my culture and even my own eyes I consider the following qualities in my physical body and mind to be flawed (name them). I repent of that attitude, my Father, because it shows lack of appreciation. I ask that You help *me* love my body in the same way that You do. I pray that You give me the eyes to stop seeing them as flaws and allow me to see the potential for good in them.

DAY 3

Embrace Testing

To Strengthen our Focus

I do not have a military background, but many of my family members who do tell me that a soldier must always remain focused on their mission. It's not only critical for the completion of the task but it's vital for keeping themselves and their unit members alive on the mission field.

My family members also share that military training is designed to help soldiers develop the strength or discipline needed to overcome the struggles and multiple distractions that may appear out there. Such training conditions them to be resilient to the variety of conditions in the environment such as excessive heat, rough accommodation, enemy bombardment. These training sessions allow them to develop the necessary skills to keep them focused on their tasks, overcome barriers and, many times, stay alive.

Scripture provides believers with similar guidance. "*No one serving as a soldier gets entangled in civilian affairs, but rather tries to please his commanding officer*" (2 Timothy 2:4). As soldiers of Christ, we can easily get caught up in the affairs of 'civilian life' when we try to meet culturally pushed agendas such as adopting the latest diet fad or taking up a specific activity, like yoga. Culturally driven self-care doesn't help us achieve our faith-based mission and it doesn't keep our fellowship with God alive. And, the enemy is always there to provide a plethora of distractions.

But, this doesn't mean we ignore taking good care of ourselves. In fact, it's quite the opposite. You see, this is God's way of telling us that our self-care should be done in such a way that we can always be ready and alert to whatever is needed to reflect the image of the Lord. God has already set our goals, and our mission is significant: to complete the Great Commission.

So, as believers, our self-care should help us stay focused on our God-given mission and purpose. Our self-care should help us overcome struggles, distractions, and barriers that interfere with taking care of ourselves. And, most importantly, our self-care should set us up to win souls for Christ.

Offering our bodies as a holy sacrifice is a way to take care of ourselves while putting God's desires first.

As I said earlier, we do this through 'faith-driven self-care.' But, please hear me. Faith-driven self-care is not a new religion or a new form of legalism. It's simply a mind and heart set of obedience to God. It is actively living out God's request in Roman's 12:1: *"Therefore, I urge you, brothers and sisters, in view of God's mercy, to offer your bodies as a living sacrifice, holy and pleasing to God--this is your true and proper worship."*

Faith-driven self-care is the method to embrace testing head-on. It is using your body, taking care of your body, or actively living in a way that pleases God putting His desires and goals first. We'll get deeper into the specifics in the next chapter.

QUICK WORKOUT: PLEASE THINK ABOUT AND ANSWER THE QUESTIONS BELOW.

What distractions, testing, or struggles do you frequently face when it comes to performing good self-care?

_____

_____

_____

To Strengthen our Willingness

Like military boot camp or training, we are given many opportunities (testings) to develop and strengthen our gifts and skills. However, we often see our training as a bad thing. We label our testing as struggles and may even call some of our efforts a form of suffering because they are so hard to endure. And, there are times when we experience pain or struggle due to the inconvenience and difficulty of the testing, even 'the derailment' of our goals and plans.

I believe we can look at many of these struggles as God's training tools to sharpen our gifts and skills for our mission for Christ. When we categorize a conflict or suffering as willingness to grow God's kingdom, it can place the *spotlight* on Christ and away from us! Realigning the spotlight allows us to keep our fellowship with God alive!

In Bill Hybels' book, *The Power of a Whisper*, he points out that "the only way God's kingdom moves forward is when a Christian is willing to take a hit."[15] Choosing to take care of ourselves for the Lord can feel like a hit. A BIG hit! But what if we could start seeing our inconveniences and suffering as the testing opportunities that God has placed in front of us? Or perhaps training to fulfill our purpose? We may feel like we are missing out on something significant in the world. But the reality is, when we choose to accept *this* hit, something significant is happening in God's kingdom!

As we provide the willingness for obedience, God equips and prepares us for the next set of tasks He sets in front of us. God equips us as we move forward in trust.

QUICK WORKOUT: PLEASE THINK ABOUT AND ANSWER THE QUESTIONS BELOW.

How does knowing that the 'hits' you experience move God's kingdom forward, strengthen your willingness to embrace testing?

_____

_____

_____

To Be Strengthened in Weakness

When we accept Jesus as our Savior, the Holy Spirit resides in us. Did you get that? We have a Person of the Holy Trinity living IN us. Our bodies are now the temple of the Holy Spirit in us (see 1 Corinthians 6:19-20).

The Holy Spirit is there to provide us with the wisdom and understanding of what we learn in God's word at the very time we need it! The Holy Spirit is God's power that should be woven into our entire lives, not just placed in one dimension or day such as Sunday. He is alive and present in real-time for us.

But, allowing this to happen, can be a struggle because we all have free will. At each decision point, we must <u>decide</u> whether to live our lives in response to the leading of the Holy Spirit, or of our own desires, our flesh – in a real sense, our ego. We have to actively turn towards the Holy Spirit to have full access to His guidance and power. John 3:6 states, *"Humans can reproduce only human life, but the Holy Spirit gives birth to spiritual life"*[16] (New Living Translation).

When our actions are driven by the Holy Spirit (and not by our flesh), we live for God's purpose. When we turn away from our egocentric desires, follow the Holy Spirit, and <u>choose</u> to take care of our body as a form of worship, we are living in obedience to God. Our obedience to the Lord helps us to be intentional in worship with our self-care. **Accepting, respecting and believing that our uniquely made body is the temple of the Holy Spirit is the gateway to offer our bodies (and our behavior change) as a holy sacrifice in obedience.**

As a Christ-follower, the fruit we receive when we allow the power of the Holy Spirit to work through our weaknesses is indescribable, and sometimes even incomprehensible. God speaks through Paul in 1

Thessalonians 5:19 and gives us specific and pointed instructions about this: "Do not quench the Spirit."

Unfortunately, not turning towards, or not accepting the Holy Spirit's power is easy to describe. It is sinful (see Galatians 5:19), <u>and it is</u> <u>***tiring***</u>. And, it does not promote wellness.

QUICK WORKOUT: PLEASE THINK ABOUT AND ANSWER THE QUESTIONS BELOW.

Here are the nine fruit of the Holy Spirit: love, joy, peace, forbearance, kindness, goodness, faithfulness, gentleness and self-control (Galatians 5:22-23).

In what ways do you feel the fruit of the Holy Spirit can help you strengthen your self-care?

_____

_____

_____

Let's pray. Father, I ask you to help me through the Holy Spirit. Please strengthen my focus, my willingness, and my weakness. I do not want to be tired. I do not want to quench the Spirit. I ask you to show me how to be well.

DAY 4

Stand with Christ

What picture do you see in your mind when you think of Jesus? Do you picture a gentle, kind, loving and forgiving Lord? Or a fierce and mighty soldier? I think most of us picture a loving and forgiving Lord Jesus. But He is a fighter, too. In fact, He is a great warrior! Jesus will go to battle for you. He loves you so much that He is *always* willing to fight for you!

Did you know that He doesn't *ever* want you to stand on your own or fight temptation alone? In fact, the primary requirement to overcome temptation is standing firm with Jesus Christ. God wants you to stay focused with Him beside you. Our firm stance with Christ helps us remain combat ready.

Unfortunately, a significant number of us are *never* combat-ready. Distractions and lack of focus interfere with our mental alertness. Sometimes we fail through direct disobedience or avoidance. It is only by focusing on Christ that we are able to recognize, and defeat temptations and distractions put in front of us. You see, when we are distracted, we are less engaged with God's purpose and become more and more focused on ourselves. The more inward-looking we are, the more stress we generate. The more stress and pressure we feel, the less value we will give to our bodies and our self-care.

Distractions don't just interfere with our self-care. Distractions ultimately interfere with the wellness of our body and, by extension, the church body and the community.

QUICK WORKOUT: PLEASE THINK ABOUT AND ANSWER THE QUESTIONS BELOW.

Think about current or recent self-care related distractions that take your gaze off of Christ. List some here.

_____

_____

_____

How are these distractions hindering you from being combat-ready and staying on God's mission?

_____

_____

_____

Spend a few minutes in prayer. What plan do you have to keep these distractions at bay?

_____

_____

_____

DAY 5

Yield Ourselves

Without a doubt, we *need* a renewed mind to be able to consistently give our bodies to God. I know I am not just speaking for myself when I say this is not an action I can complete by my own thinking or efforts.

However, I can also say that *it is possible* to allow the Lord to renew our thinking. My thinking was renewed through reading God's word, spending time with God in fellowship and prayer, singing praise music, listening to sermons, and seeking godly counsel as needed. My thinking about the way I took care of myself also changed, I think, because I felt led to pray for it to change.

Another way of saying this is that I learned how to trust (and respond) to the Lord's will with my self-care choices and actions. Do I take care of myself perfectly? Definitely not. But, my self-care, and life, has changed dramatically. That's why I believe it can change yours, too!

Let's go back to our verse from this chapter for our last study points. Romans 12:2 reads, *"Do not conform to the pattern of this world, but be transformed by the renewing of your mind. Then you will be able to test and approve what God's will is—his good, pleasing and perfect will."* Paul tells us *how* to become a holy and living sacrifice (from Romans 12:1). He says we must yield our thoughts, our will, and our desires by letting God *continually* renew our mind and allowing the power of the Holy Spirit to work in, or through us, to transform us.

So, what will this look like operationally, that is, in action, if we give Him our minds and replace our personal or cultural thoughts with His thoughts? The ESV study bible describes it as living alive with Christ (from being dead) or living in a way that pleases Christ by offering our whole self, body, and soul.

Bible commentators give some operating examples of God having our minds and wills:

- If the world controls our thinking we are a conformer. If God controls our thinking we are a transformer.[17]
- Knowing what is good, pleasing to God, and perfect provides the guidelines for discerning the will of God. Paul applies these guidelines to **discern** the will of God in different circumstances. As we apply the guidelines we allow God's will to penetrate more and more of our daily life.[18]
- "What is 'good' is helpful to people and conforms to the moral standard revealed by God. **'Perfect' means to use our gifts, resources, and opportunities for maximum effect in God's kingdom.**"[19]

These acts of giving God our mind and will help us become a holy and living sacrifice. This means we make ourselves an offering that is not only set apart from profane matters but also **dedicated to His service**. Remember, Jesus is our living example in the New Testament.

Note the word 'discern' in the second bullet point. Look up 'discern' in the dictionary and write the definition here:

_____

75

Theologians give some operating examples of God having our body:

"The presenting of the body to God implies not only the avoiding of the sins that are committed with or against the body, but using of the body as a servant of the soul in the service of God."[20]

To offer a *holy* sacrifice (Romans 12:1), our offering must be free of moral defilement. To do so, requires that we abstain from defilement to or with our body. The renewing of our minds allows us to turn to the fruit of the Holy Spirit to help us do this.

Galatians 5 contrasts the acts of the flesh with the fruit of the spirit:

The acts of the flesh are obvious: sexual immorality, impurity, and debauchery; idolatry and witchcraft; hatred, discord, jealousy, fits of rage, selfish ambition, dissensions, factions and envy; drunkenness, orgies, and the like. I warn you, as I did before, that those who live like this will not inherit the kingdom of God.

But the fruit of the Spirit is love, joy, peace, forbearance, kindness, goodness, faithfulness, gentleness and self-control. Against such things there is no law (Galatians 5:19-23).

We can see that God offers a better way than our own self-efforts. God knows our sinfulness but loves us so much He gives us a path to help us avoid sin. The path is when we actively participate in becoming the temple of the Holy Spirit *and also* worship Him through that process.

We can't do this if we stand alone.

God has set this up as a win-win for us. However, it may only be discernible after our perspective is transformed, and we see the good according to God's will. We are all created with areas of strength and weakness and can count on the fact that Satan will attack our weaknesses. For many of us, comparing ourselves to others or to a perfect worldly standard (that doesn't exist) constantly gets in our way. It does not lend to a new way of thinking.

For instance, starving ourselves or performing stringent exercise to look shapely does not bring about wellness. In fact, it interferes with our welfare. While these rules and their applications seem wise because they require intense devotion, pious self-denial, and severe bodily discipline, they provide no help in conquering a person's evil desires (See Colossians 2:23). Scripture shows us that our cravings for pleasure and sensory satisfaction are deeply rooted in our sinful desires like pride, envy, lust of the flesh. These desires can be expressed in daily self-care habits. Sadly, the long-term effects of these patterns and self-care habits can present as health symptoms and conditions that may, and typically do, progress to disease.

QUICK WORKOUT: PLEASE THINK ABOUT AND ANSWER THE QUESTIONS BELOW.

Romans 12:1-2 commands us to PRESENT our bodies as a living sacrifice and NOT conform to the pattern of this world. In effect, we are asked to obey before we understand.

What value do you see in obeying before understanding?

_____

_____

_____

What barriers do you see?

_____

_____

_____

Spend a few moments in quiet prayer. How can you overcome the barriers you listed above?

_____

_____

_____

A Promise from God

I pray that you see the hope and potential wellness that I saw in God's request to direct to Him *"our true and proper worship"* (See Romans 12:1). In addition to the grace of salvation, He also provides a way to turn away from our sins on a daily basis. Praise and remembrance help us submit to the Holy Spirit's power to fight temptation. I pray that offering yourself as a holy and living sacrifice opens the door to the understanding of His instructions and for His Word to become alive in you.

> *Do not waste time arguing over godless ideas and old wives' tales. Instead, train yourself to be godly. Physical training is good, but training for godliness is much better,* **promising benefits in this life and in the life to come.** *This is a trustworthy saying, and everyone should accept it. This is why we work hard and continue to struggle, for our hope is in the living God, who is the Savior of all people and particularly of all believers* (1 Timothy 4:7-10, emphasis added)

As a believer and follower of Christ, we have a personal responsibility to reject every false teaching that undermines our faith, and train ourselves by reading God's word on a regular basis. This is meant to be a continuous action, so we move forward and grow in our training or understanding. While exercise, restraint in eating certain foods or avoidance of specific behaviors are of value, there are limits to our self-discipline. But there is **no limit to the power** of the Holy Spirit, to cause us to avoid sin in our lives, and bring Christ to people.

QUICK WORKOUT: PLEASE THINK ABOUT AND ANSWER THE QUESTIONS BELOW.

Why is the responsibility to train ourselves to be godly on us and not God?

_____

_____

_____

What do you need to start hearing and doing differently today to be able to receive the promise of 1 Timothy 4:7-10?

_____

_____

_____

Can you think of any barriers to your doing this?

_____

_____

_____

Pray that your focus remains on God, so you can perform the above action(s) and receive the promises of this verse.

RECAP

How do you renew your thinking?

- Allow Transformation to Begin
- Fear God
- Embrace Testing
- Stand with Christ
- Yield yourself

When your thinking changes, your behavior changes, too!

Accepting, respecting and believing that our uniquely made body is the temple of the Holy Spirit is the gateway to offering our bodies as a holy sacrifice in obedience and allowing Him to change our behavior.

My challenge to you is to keep reading and learning how to use your renewed perspective to adjust your self-care behavior.

Chapter 3

Transform Your Behavior for Faith-driven Self-care

You remember that I decided to start running at the gym when I first stayed home with my daughter. I forgot to tell you that I was 39 years old at the time, and I had never run before.

And I also shared that at that time, I only went to the gym for company. Not knowing how to use the machines or weights, I decided that running was the least dangerous activity to attempt. I had no idea how it was going to turn out – being 'so old' with no experience. I didn't think of myself as a runner, so I guess I thought I had nothing to lose.

But, honestly, I didn't think I had anything to gain either. My belief was that, because I had never been a runner before, it was silly to believe I could become one at this stage. However, the reality was that this was just *my opinion.* It wasn't a fact.

Dictionary.com defines 'opinion' as 'a view or judgment formed about something, not necessarily based on fact or knowledge.' In other words, my opinion was nothing more than an inference. It certainly wasn't based on evidence. A specific answer to this question wouldn't be found in a reference site or book. If I looked up whether no experience (except for illness or injury) was a reason for failing at running, I would not find sufficient evidence for that. Furthermore, if I asked 20 people about my running potential, there would be 20 slightly different answers. Thus, the conclusion must be that my opinion of my running potential was not a provable fact.

That's the interesting thing about facts. They are provable (with books, science, measurements, maps, etc.). Facts occur when the same observation can be made by multiple people. We all know what facts are and can state plenty of examples of them. Facts could include the names of the constellations, the parts of a plant cell, the colors in the rainbow, names of dog breeds, the capital of a state, or the colors of the human iris. So, generally speaking, opinions *are not* facts.

Therefore, if you follow my train of thought even further, *I could* call my opinion about myself **fiction**. You see, that's what happened to me. When I realized my opinion about my running potential was just a story I was telling myself, my eyes were able to see the facts, or the truth. So, when I started to replace my fiction with the truth, I started to see where I, or, more importantly, gave God the opportunity to change my story.

And I was completely humbled because *I did indeed become a runner!*

I'm not the first person to experience this. As a nurse, I've seen this shift happen many times, especially while patients were making lifestyle modifications. Let me tell you, working with patients who have been told they need to change their lifestyle has taught me some things about fiction, fact, truth – and humility.

The most relevant point here is that nobody (including me!) ever wants to hear that they have to change their lifestyle or give up something they consider to be good. It's just too painful to even think about trying to survive without it!

As a result, when the time came to talk to my patients about their lifestyle changes, we usually came out of those talks with the patient stating an understanding, *and a willingness* to eat differently, exercise, manage their stress or disease as their doctor requested. But at heart we both thought and *believed they weren't going to be able to do it.*

If I pressed further into why my patients thought this way, they would tell me their opinions:

- They just couldn't see themselves making it work because they couldn't make it work before.
- They couldn't see where or how they could make any changes.
- It seemed impossible because of the 'hated' food they knew they should eat, or the 'hated' exercise prescribed.

But do you see it? Most of the time their statements were only about the barriers to the desired change. But these statements contained not an iota of fact or truth. It followed that they had no hope in the success of the change.

For that patient to find success, a paradigm shift had to occur in their mind first. They had to accept a new and fundamental belief that they could learn to live another way. If they continued to believe their own opinions that they would never learn to manage their stress or disease, like eating healthy food or adopting the habit of exercise, a change would *never* happen.

But, with new beliefs, a change could happen overnight. They only needed a fresh view, or a renewed look at the facts and fiction, opinions and truth, plus the humility to accept it. If they could walk forward with humility, they would experience a paradigm shift. Once this paradigm shift occurred, the patients would have success from the word "Go." In my case, as soon as I experienced this paradigm shift as an amateur runner, I realized I could be a runner.

Now, let's apply this concept to our discussion about faith-driven self-care. When believers allow their thinking to be renewed by God, a paradigm shift occurs through the hope of Christ. Lives, behaviors, and lifestyles can change in amazing ways. God shows us the truth through His Word. When the Word becomes alive in our hearts, it replaces our opinions or the fictional stories we tell ourselves. When we experience *this* paradigm shift: the belief that the blood of Christ DOES save us, that Jesus IS our Savior, and that the word of God and the power of the Holy Spirit are REAL and CAN change us, most of us get excited. We desire a more in-depth understanding of God's word. We look for revelation when our eyes alight on a passage of scripture. We want to be changed.

On the other hand, we can all think of times where we have read a verse over and over and over without it speaking to us. Sometimes it could be that God is waiting for another time to open our hearts to that verse. But most times sin, like pride, can block our understanding. Our pride strives for attention and glory, which <u>we</u> rob from God. The truths of scripture can remain unseen when we hang onto pride because it interferes with the prompting of the Holy Spirit.

Thankfully, God has provided us the virtue of humility as the tool to loosen the tight grip pride has on our minds and wills. Let's explore how we can become humble before God.

How to Transform Behavior

DAY 1

Humility

Our core self struggles with humility, but God shows His power by requesting a simple act of obedience. Let's begin by looking at a passage about humility.

This story, in 2 Kings 5:8-15, is the account of how a highly renowned Syrian commander named Naaman is healed. Although Naaman has military expertise, he faces a battle for his life against the incurable disease of leprosy. At one point when Naaman knows he has no other solution but to seek healing, he journeys to Israel to get help from the king of Israel. The prophet Elisha steps in and instructs the king of Israel to send Naaman to him instead.

It gets interesting when Naaman arrives at Elisha's door expecting the prophet to come and minister to such an important personage as him personally. We'll pick up there in the passage.

> But Elisha sent a messenger out to him with this message: "Go and wash yourself seven times in the Jordan River. Then your skin will be restored, and you will be healed of your leprosy." But Naaman became angry and stalked away. "I thought he would certainly come out to meet me!" he said. "I expected him to wave his hand over the leprosy

and call on the name of the Lord his God and heal me! Aren't the rivers of Damascus, the Abana and the Pharpar, better than any of the rivers of Israel? Why shouldn't I wash in them and be healed?" So Naaman turned and went away in a rage.

But his officers tried to reason with him and said, "Sir, if the prophet had told you to do something very difficult, wouldn't you have done it? So you should certainly obey him when he says simply, 'Go and wash and be cured!'" So Naaman went down to the Jordan River and dipped himself seven times, as the man of God had instructed him. And his skin became as healthy as the skin of a young child, and he was healed! Then Naaman and his entire party went back to find the man of God. They stood before him and Naaman said, "Now I know that there is no God in all the world except in Israel" (2 Kings 5:10-15a).

God already had a plan, a treatment, or a prescription for Naaman's disease. But Naaman didn't want to follow it. He was annoyed, even angry and *insulted* at the simplicity of God's instructions. Naaman wanted something big and showy, something worthy of his status, worthy of God's status, too. Naaman's obedience, through that simple act of self-care, vividly reflects how we should respond to God. "God isn't interested in the giving of our grand, worldly gestures. He desires our simple, everyday faithfulness. These actions bring God joy," says Robert Varner, Youth Minister of South Gate Baptist Church.[21]

After Naaman was finally persuaded to follow Elisha's instructions, that of dipping seven times in the most polluted of rivers, the Jordan, he was totally healed. And, after his healing, he glorified God by announcing his belief in God "as the one and only God." We, too, desire to get rid of our sickness of sin. We want and desire spiritual healing. I can think of many times where I have reasoned that a big ceremonial activity or a formal observance was what I needed to do to be right with God, to be healed from my sin. Or I have silently taken advantage of God's grace, done nothing, and presumed I would be forgiven regardless of the absence of my humility or repentance. I wanted to cling to my pride and not be exposed in public.

But, to experience humility with God, we must love Him completely. We cannot "divorce our internal hearts from our external actions," says Paul Washer, in *A Living and Holy Sacrifice*, citing Romans 12:1-2, on Youtube. If God has our heart, He has our body too![22]

Many times, when I present the idea of faith-driven self-care, or giving our body to God, people love the idea. Even more so after I explain that doing so provides a powerful motivation to improve self-care follow-through. And then they always ask that same question: "Great! I'm on board! How do I do this? I *need* to start eating healthier!"

My response is always a buzz kill. "Spend time with God and let Him break you. Let God tear you apart and show you who you really are compared to Him." He did that to Job and that transformed his perspective of God totally. If you let Him, He will do it to you, too.

QUICK WORKOUT: PLEASE THINK ABOUT AND ANSWER THE QUESTIONS BELOW.

How did humility affect Naaman's outcome?

_____

_____

_____

Why did God have to deal with Namaan's character before He healed him?

_____

_____

_____

Let's pray together. Lord, show me where I am prideful. I want to follow you and obey. Reveal the areas where I need to address my pride.

In what way do you need humility for your healing?

_____

_____

_____

DAY 2

Be with God

For so many of us, while we want our lives to be better, we also fear the mere scintilla of change – any change!

We say we want to take better care of ourselves: we want to eat healthier; we want to feel less stress; we want to do the things God commands in scripture. We may even say we want to give our body to God as a form of worship. We say these things, but...there's always a but. We say, I want to do…this action…**but** I don't think I can give up…this thing. We 'can't' give it up! So, we do nothing. For change to occur in us, we have to show our trust through our actions, not just in how we feel. For example, to experience joy in His refuge, we have to live out the motions of tasting and seeing that the Lord is good (Psalm 34:8).

When we cling to our worldly 'fictitious' ideas of what is good, it interferes with our choices and our acts of will. This <u>changes</u> the quality of our offering. Our offering reflects our lack of trust, or, more bluntly, our unbelief. We don't trust that which God is telling us to do is the best solution for us.

Paul's words in Philippians 2:12-13 remind us why we should trust in God's plan.

Therefore, my dear friends, as you have always obeyed—not only in my presence but now much more in my absence—continue to work out your salvation with fear

and trembling, for it is God who works in you to will and
to act in order to fulfill his good purpose.

I believe this exhortation helps us to remember *why* we should trust God's truth. It is because our purpose is to live out God's purpose and use our gifts to expand His kingdom.

But then there's the million-dollar question. How? How do we start the making of a paradigm shift when we decide to use faith-driven self-care as a form of worship?

The answer is simple: spend time with God. What an awesome privilege when we begin to know some of His attributes!

The Attributes of God

Omnipotence
Omnipotence means that God is all-powerful. As believers, we believe that God has supreme power. We believe God has the authority to do what He wants to fulfill His plan. God has power over everything. He is not physically limited like a man or woman. His power is infinite. He has power over everything – including nature and physics.

Omniscience
Omniscience means that God is all-knowing. As believers, we acknowledge that God is all-knowing of the past, present and future. His knowledge is complete. He knows all that there is to know. Nothing is a surprise to God.

Omnipresence

Omnipresence means that God is all-present. As believers, we believe in the mystery that God has the capability of being everywhere at the same time. It encompasses the entire universe. He is everywhere at once.

When we accept salvation, we are free from the burden of our sins from yesterday, today and the future. Therefore, our bodies are a worthy sacrifice to the Lord. Without an understanding of this truth, we would live in despair and without hope. It is the people with an understanding of this truth who will prosper (Proverbs 19:8).

Just as it is appropriate to make lifestyle changes one step at a time, God allows us to learn and grow one step at a time when we offer our bodies to God as a living sacrifice. The Holy Spirit tells us what to do to offer ourselves and provides us with the wisdom, understanding, counsel, fortitude, knowledge, fervor, and the fear of the Lord as needed.

Faith and trust, however, are required. We do have to believe and trust that God's way is better, even when we do not know what that will look like for us in the end. If we focus on the physical aspects of how hard changing our self-care will be, well, we will get in the way of our own success.

When the Pharisees asked Jesus which was the greatest commandment, Jesus replied: *"Love the Lord your God with all your heart and with all your soul and with all your mind. This is the first and greatest commandment"* (Matthew 22:37-38).

I suspect that, like me, you will likely have fears and doubts when you decide to use faith-driven self-care as a form of worship. It may not feel natural at first. For one thing, it sounds too good to be true. Worship and praise are uplifting actions, while we may be used to condemning ourselves when we think about our self-care.

But the truth is that it can be and is all right to have an uplifting and even a motivating way to take better care of ourselves. God wants us to be well. When we become humble, we can put our faith in the attributes of God, not on our limitations. We can find hope through the love of Christ. We <u>can trust</u> we will be changed.

Our single act of humility will allow God to raise up and maintain a strong army of soldiers.

QUICK WORKOUT: PLEASE THINK ABOUT AND ANSWER THE QUESTIONS BELOW.

Which of the three attributes of God (omnipotence, omniscience, or omnipresence) is most comforting to you?

_____

_____

_____

How do you think the attributes of God could be helpful to you as you practice faith-driven self-care?

_____

_____

_____

Spend a few moments praising God for His attributes and showing Him your adoration.

DAY 3

Grateful Fasting

As a nurse, I'm aware you may have already decided you want to skip today's reading – just from seeing the title. I get it. I've heard patients respond to the dreaded pre-op orders of "no food or drinks after midnight." I know how people feel about it. Do you have any idea how many patients go to a fast food joint at 11:30 p.m. for a BIG burger and a refreshing Mountain Dew the night before the procedure? A lot!

And, I know *how I feel* about fasting too! Especially fasting at church.

I don't even know a word to describe my response after hearing 'fasting.' It's a combination of the feeling of dread, a deep sigh combined with voicing the sound "ugh," and heavily slumped shoulders. No, fasting is never a popular topic. Not in the healthcare arena. Not in self-care. And not at church. We all like a full belly. It's comfortable.

Well, have you ever noticed how pride and satisfied stomachs are familiar companions in the Bible, too? Or what about how close hunger and temptation live? Pride is a real struggle for us physically, just as it is emotionally. Take a look at the easy-to-remember stories about eating the forbidden fruit (See Genesis 3) or how God humbled the Israelites with hunger in the wilderness (See Deuteronomy 8:2, 3) to demonstrate the power of our hunger and the quick presence of Satan's 'simple fixes' <u>that easily distract us from our mission.</u>

Thankfully, God has provided us with a means for personal sanctification. Yes, fasting is one of the means of personal sanctification. And, yes, it requires gratitude to appreciate its ability to humble us.

Arthur Wallis, author of *God's Chosen Fast A Spiritual and Practical Guide to Fasting*, offers tremendous insight into spiritual fasting and humility. He describes fasting as "a discipline of the body with a tendency to humble the soul."[23] Wallis writes that fasting can be used as a time for spiritual examination, time to spend with God, and time to focus on kingdom growth. We tend to think of our obsession or lack of discipline with food as an issue peculiar to our times. But, even back in 1968, Wallis observed, "There are those who are seemingly oblivious to their bondage to food and to the fact that there is a leakage of spiritual power."[24]

The humility we find through our obedience to fasting lies opposite of the pride we exhibit through our hunger, our lust. Fasting is pivotal to us becoming, and remaining, mission capable. When we perform this action through love for Christ, our actions show our genuine obedience.

Wallis reminds us that "in giving us the privilege of fasting as well as praying, God has added a powerful weapon to our spiritual armory."

The trouble is we don't fast often enough in the church. Wallis comments that fasting in the church didn't disappear because it lacked success. It disappeared because it shifted from God-driven spiritual intercession and became an obligation. In other words, it became legalistic.[25]

What is the biblical perspective? *Does Jesus want us to fast?*

Yes. He expects it!

The verses in Matthew 6:1-18 give clear guidance from Jesus on giving, praying *and fasting.*

- 6:2 *"So when you give to the needy..."*
- 6:5 *"And when you pray..."*
- 6:16-18: *"When you fast..."*

"When you fast, do not look somber as the hypocrites do, for they disfigure their faces to show others they are fasting. Truly I tell you, they have received their reward in full. But when you fast, put oil on your head and wash your face, so that it will not be obvious to others that you are fasting, but only to your Father, who is unseen; and your Father, who sees what is done in secret, will reward you."

Jesus said *when* you fast. Fasting is expected of you, the same way giving, and praying are. I think the modern-day church knows all about giving and praying, but I'm not sure I've seen much teaching on the need to fast.

What do *you* think?

QUICK WORKOUT: PLEASE THINK ABOUT AND ANSWER THE QUESTIONS BELOW.

What reservations come to your mind when thinking about performing a fast? Check all that apply.

☐ Old Testament practice; no longer relevant	☐ Don't have the discipline or stamina	☐ Interferes with my work	☐ Don't see the point of it
☐ Religious ritual	☐ Unable to go without food for long hours	☐ Interferes with family life	☐ History of breaking fasts; fear of failure
☐ Not taught in my church	☐ Will exacerbate my medical condition	☐ No one to fast with me	☐ Haven't heard from God

Reflect on what you've discovered about yourself a few moments. How do you feel about these barriers? If you had several reservations, so did I. Let me share my story.

DAY 4

The Prompting of the Holy Spirit

A few years ago, I had the opportunity to be on a pastor search team for our church. I had no idea what to expect but agreed to join the other eight people on the team for an almost two-year-journey. Midway through, the group leader asked us if we would be willing to commit to a 24-hour fast with the goal of hearing from the Holy Spirit as a united group of believers.

I felt somewhat blindsided. Suddenly, I felt weirdly 'not Christian' enough. To this day I'm not sure I can articulate exactly why. For one thing, I was afraid to fast. Not so much because I thought I was going to starve to death but because I didn't think I could do it 'right.' I had a young child at home and was juggling a lot of projects, so I couldn't afford to be running around hungry and biting everyone's head off all day. But, even more so, I felt ill-equipped to fast. I didn't know how to focus on hearing from the Holy Spirit. I didn't even know that one needed to fast for that purpose.

Thankfully, our leader did a wonderful job of walking us through the process. First, we as a team, and then individually, spent some time in prayer to determine if we were called to fast. We each had the option to say no, or that we weren't called. Of course, I felt called. Yep, I felt called to fast. (At first, I was so bummed!) We decided on a day for all of us to do the fast together. We talked about our fears of fasting and our leader provided some guidance based on his last personal fast and gave us some literature.

We fasted. I spent time in prayer. I spent time in scripture. I spent time in repentance. By the end of the fast I was deeply humbled. And do you know what else? I survived the fast. Not only that, our team became singly focused on the same goal: hearing from God through the Holy Spirit.

And we did! We moved forward on our journey and were led to our next pastor. I tell you the truth: that 24-hour fast changed me.

Fasting

Going back to the book, *God's Chosen Fast: A Spiritual and Practical Guide to Fasting*, Wallis describes a natural sequence in the Old Testament of fasting from a self-humbling purpose to the mourning of self-repentance and contrition. This transition caused the Israelites to look at fasting as an equivalent to mourning. Wallis writes, "Mourning over personal sin and failure is an indispensable stage in the process of sanctification, and it is facilitated by fasting. However, God wants to bring us beyond the place of mourning only for our personal sins, to where we are moved by the Spirit to mourn for the sins of the Church, the nation, and even the world."[26]

Wallis also points us to Matthew 6:5-18, where Jesus teaches us to give, pray and fast. In Jesus' teaching, fasting is a separate intercession from prayer. Although they can be spiritual exercises used together, they can have separate purposes, too. The point is that Jesus taught it with the expectation that His followers would be obedient to the prompting of the Spirit.[27]

"Spiritual truths go ignored without the prompting of the Holy Spirit," Wallis explains. Fasting helps with the prompting of the Holy

Spirit as the "divine correction to the pride of the human heart" and because it is the "God-appointed means for the flowing of His grace and power." In other words, it's the way to humility. He goes on to explain that it is now not just an "act of mourning, but an act of preparation for the return of Jesus." This fasting then, when God-initiated or God-ordained, becomes part of our restoration and renewal as well as our heavenly mission (See Ezra 8:21; Acts 13:3;14:23).

Fasting can and should be used with prayer. Fasting with prayer displays prayer in earnest so that the prayer warrior will not give up. Fasting with prayer is using a means God has chosen to make our voice rise to heaven.[28]

Our pastor search team spent quite a bit of time prior to the fast repenting of our sins, and the sins of the church. We *were* in mourning. The church we knew was no longer the same. As we progressed through the prayer and fasting process, we mourned for the nation, even the world, to some extent. We met once or twice a week and we spent several weeks praying like this before our 24-hour fast. I don't know if we made an impact in the hearts of the people in the nation and the world. But I do know the process made an impact on the hearts of folks in the room.

After our pastor search team fasted individually as a team, our team leader requested a church-wide 24-hour fast. We felt like we had good participation, and after the fast it seemed like we had a smoother journey, especially as we began the selection process.

The act of fasting in search of humility also releases the apostolic power needed to overcome enemy attack.

Wallis points us to a specific scripture when humility through fasting was called nationally (publicly) to overcome a threat or crisis. All of these missions, without exception, were answered and victorious.

- King Jehoshaphat's army was victorious against an invasion of Judah (2 Chronicles 20:1-30).
- Ezra was protected on his journey back to Jerusalem with the temple items (Ezra 8:21-23).
- The people of Nineveh were spared God's destruction (Jonah 3:6-10).

QUICK WORKOUT: PLEASE THINK ABOUT AND ANSWER THE QUESTIONS BELOW.

What is your experience with being sensitive to the prompting of the Holy Spirit?

_____

_____

_____

Over the next day, prayerfully ponder whether you would be willing to fast to be more sensitive to His prompting?

_____

_____

_____

DAY 5

Trust in God's Promises

I share all of the above information about fasting to validate the value of the fasting process. I believe private or individual fasting has an important place in our self-care regimens.

We are all given spiritual gifts and a calling. We have a purpose for our time on earth. A 24-fast is a spiritual way to become humble, make us more sensitive to the promptings of the Holy Spirit, and make a faith-based connection between the wellness of your body and your mission for Christ. Whether you want to consider a spiritual fast a starting place, a reset fast, or even a 'detox,' a 24-hour fast can pack a lot of change into this little act of obedience.

At the time of our search team fast, our team was called to the mission of finding a new pastor. We started with the goal of a team burdened with humility. Without achieving humility, I do not believe we would have completed our call so successfully.

I refer again to author Arthur Wallis, who leads us to scripture which provides examples when humility through fasting (privately) prepared them for their mission, allowed individuals to complete their missions, or allowed the fulfillment of God's mission.

- Daniel's plea for God's fulfillment of His promise and restoration of Jerusalem (Daniel 9:2)

- Elijah's spiritual preparation and the saving of the widow and her son (1 Kings 17)
- Jesus' fast before overcoming temptation, before the start of His ministry (Matthew 4:1-11)

In Scripture, Paul speaks about this topic of humility, in particular relation to the use of our spiritual gifts. Our need to be humble and walk by faith is our next verse of focus:

> *For by the grace given me I say to every one of you: Do not think of yourself more highly than you ought, but rather think of yourself with sober judgment, in accordance with the faith God has distributed to each of you* (Romans 12:3).

Paul's words remind us to not boast about our gifts, not to covet another's gifts and also not to underuse them. We are also instructed to use our gifts for God's glory because our gifts come from God, and they are to be used for His purpose. To do this, we have to remain humble. Not being humble before God, puts us in a position where we think we know what is best.[29]

We look for the continuous renewing of our minds, so we know what is good and so that Christ can continue His work through us. Our faith and our position in Christ allow us to overcome distractions and stay on course for the Great Commission, which Christ has perfectly positioned His church to fulfill.

Although everyone's prayer conversations will be different, center your intentions on the goal of humility. Ask God specifically if you are honest about your perception and use of your spiritual gifts. Pray that God provides you with a clear direction in your fast. And do so without grumbling.

There are three types of fasting.

- Absolute fasting – fast from all food and drink, typically a fast of three days or less
- Normal fasting – fast from all food and beverages, water permitted. May last an extended amount of time...Jesus fasted for 40 days
- Partial fasting – fast by a restriction of diet; an omission of a type of food or a specific meal per day or only one specific food for a specific time period

It is probable that some of us will feel the burden of an absolute fast lie heavy on our hearts. Some of us will be led to a normal fast, and then others will be led to a partial fast.

Read the following scriptures and consider the ways humility impacts the experience of the person in the verse. Then consider whether the outcome would have been the same without humility.

Romans 4:20
Matthew 6:16-18
Matthew 6:24

The next verse speaks to the humility of choosing God over idols. This decision isn't a one-time choice but a choice to be made over and over. Read Joshua 24:15-23.

We love to focus on ourselves. We are prideful about many things, and our enemy uses a combination of our prideful attitudes to viciously attack and diminish the quality of the self-care to our bodies, the Holy Spirit's temple. Our pride keeps our focus on ourselves and our own needs, and not on the needs of others. Our enemy takes us off course by interfering with our combat readiness and impacting kingdom growth!

I will close this section with the words of Linda Dillow author of *Satisfy My Thirsty Soul* who wrote, "The Lord delights when I tell him that I love Him, but Jesus made it clear that if my words of love are authentic, I will live out my love by obeying His commands. Obedience motivated by love differs greatly from obedience motivated by duty."[30]

A Promise from God

Whichever way we choose to fast, it can free us from the bondage of pride and help us to find humility. More than that, it helps us understand how God wants us to use our gifts and experience the quickening of our hearts through Scripture and prayer.

To learn the answer, we should start by asking God to show us how we are progressing in using our gifts for His mission. Listen to whether the Holy Spirit is prompting us to fast and then ask what form of fasting is appropriate for us.

> *Don't be impressed with your own wisdom. Instead, fear the Lord and turn away from evil. Then you will have healing for your body and strength for your bones* (Proverbs 3:7-8).

Proverbs 3:7-8 and Philippians 2:12-13 (from Day 2) remind us of our purpose. They encourage us to involve the Holy Spirit when we make decisions regarding our body or mind and the use of our gifts. In particular, we are not to think of ourselves more highly than we ought. We should apply this concept to our decision-making capability. We should not think that we alone have the wisdom, the moral stature, or the breadth of knowledge needed to discern God's will by ourselves. We should seek guidance through the Holy Spirit at all times.

Whatever the outcome, the prompting of any fasting by the Holy Spirit should not be ignored or watered down to a more comfortable experience. We must believe that if we are prompted to fast, the Holy

Spirit will sustain us. We cannot let our fear of hunger, irritability and other discomforts, scheduling conflicts, others' perceptions, or even our thoughts of giving up or failing the fast attempt interfere with fasting. Doing this will put us right back to where we think we are wiser than God, which puts us back into being the easy target of our enemy.

QUICK WORKOUT: PLEASE THINK ABOUT AND ANSWER THE QUESTIONS BELOW.

Spend some time in prayer. Do you feel the Lord calling you to a fast?

_____

_____

_____

When will you implement the fast? Spend a few minutes planning your fast.

_____

_____

_____

ADDITIONAL QUESTIONS TO PRAY THROUGH AS YOU PREPARE TO IMPLEMENT YOUR FAST.

Which of your spiritual gifts are mostly in operation?

_____

_____

_____

When do you generally use them?

_____

_____

_____

When you use your spiritual gifts, do you lean on the Holy Spirit for guidance?

_____

_____

_____

RECAP

How do you transform your behavior?

- Humility
- Being in God's presence
- Fasting
- Prompting of the Holy Spirit
- Trusting in God's Promises

When you experience humility, the Holy Spirit will guide your thoughts and behavior.

Humbly spending time with God, letting Him break you and showing you who you really are so you can see who God really is serves as a catalyst for the change in the self-care behavior you desire.

If you have been called to fast, my challenge to you is to implement the fast with the goal of achieving humility. I promise you will be changed.

Chapter 4

Apply it to Self-care

While researching for this book, I randomly stumbled onto the following quote which shook me to my core. I cried like a baby when I read it. I couldn't believe how much I could relate to this woman describing why people living in poverty make the decisions they do.

> "We have learned not to try too hard to be middle class. It never works out well and always makes you feel worse for having tried and failed yet again. Better not to try. It makes more sense to get food that you know will be palatable and cheap and that keeps well. Junk food is a pleasure that we are allowed to have; why would we give that up? We have very few of them."

She goes on,

> "Nobody gives thought to depression. You have to understand that we know that we will never not feel

tired. We will never feel hopeful. We will never get a vacation. Ever. We know that the very act of being poor guarantees that we will never not be poor. It doesn't give us much reason to improve ourselves...There isn't much point trying."[31]

Reading this makes me feel so sad and empty that my heart hurts for hers. Life is always difficult for people who live in poverty. But, while I am sad about her situation and my heart aches for those facing poverty, there's something else going on, too. I feel like I connect with the *emptiness* this woman feels, although I have never lived in financial poverty.

My connection with this woman is in a different realm. I can't explain it other than to say I believe the Lord wanted me to see this other connection. Please see what I 'read' in this quote.

> "I have learned not to try too hard to be a godly person. It never works out well and always makes me feel worse for having tried and failed yet again. Better not to try. It makes more sense to stay in the life that I know will be accepted – no matter how I (or others) think of myself. Living for myself is a pleasure that I'm allowed to have; why would I give that up? I have very few of them."

And then,

> "Nobody gives thought to depression. You have to understand that I know that I will never not feel less

than. I will never feel hopeful. I will never get forgiveness for what I've done. Ever. I know that the very act of being a bad person guarantees that I will never not be a bad person. It doesn't give me much reason to improve myself. I don't try to do it for others because I know I will do something wrong...there isn't much point trying."

I *have* lived in a state of poverty of the spirit. And I was a resident there, even as a believer in God, for a long, long time. Sadly, I wasn't living there alone. And, we were exhausted citizens.

How to Apply it to Self-care

DAY 1

Admit You Need God for Self-care

When I first started talking to people about what I learned in Romans 12:1-2, I had an excitement I hadn't felt before. I knew it was a life-saving find for me.

But, I had such a hard time articulating what I was trying to say. Of course, I thought I was making perfect sense. Except, people would ask me the strangest questions:

- Is this a weight-loss program?
- Are you talking about eating healthy?
- Aren't you just talking about faith?
- How are you going to compete with Weightwatchers, or any other weight-loss program?

That last one was my favorite. I wasn't trying to compete with or outdo anything. I was seeking freedom from all of the exhausting trappings of taking better care of myself – and hoping to help other people do the same.

As I mentioned in an earlier chapter, I felt like I was always 'fighting' to keep up my motivation – and my precious time – to take care of myself. I refused to believe that the constant fatigue I was experiencing was what God wanted for me as I served Him. I was convinced that God would not give me the spiritual gift of service and expect me to serve, being so tired all of the time. So, I was elated to find an effective weapon for my struggle.

But, ironically, freedom from this fatigue came only after I realized I *needed* God. And, specifically, I needed Him to help me balance *my service* and *my self-care*.

When we become Christ followers, we learn that we will always be a group of 'sinners.' We're all 'bad people' and we've all done things that cause us to fall short of the glory of God. The result of our sin is separation from God. But, *thank God*, there's the Good News! We learn about the deep *agape* love God has for us when we understand that, even though we have sinned against God, through repentance and accepting Jesus as our Savior, we are saved from the eternal separation from God that we deserve. We are <u>given</u> God's gift of grace – mercy and forgiveness. It is nothing we deserve or can ever earn.

I love watching a new believer accept Christ. I'm always moved by their tears after they realize they are forgiven *only because* God loves *them* so much that He sent His only Son, Jesus, to die *for them*, so *they* would have eternal life. They let go of their selfishness and see how they are truly nothing without God. None of us are.

Of course, the scenario I've described is certainly not new to us as believers. I reiterated this because I want to make the point that, when we come to, or accept Christ into our lives, we also have to come to that place where we acknowledge our own sin and *spiritual emptiness*. We have to realize <u>we need</u> God.

We *need* God's blessing in Christ, the promise of the Spirit who will dwell within us as a believer. It's through the Spirit that we can experience a relationship with God in an intimate and personal way and have access to the power and strength of God to complete the tasks we're asked to do.

I love what Billy Graham says about this concept: "In other words, when we come to God, we must realize our own sin and our spiritual emptiness and poverty. We must not be self-satisfied or proud in our hearts, thinking we don't really need God. If we are, God cannot bless us. The Bible says, "*God opposes the proud but gives grace to the humble*" (James 4:6).[32] Reverend Graham stated that God cannot bless us if we think we don't need God. Oh, It's a wonderful day when a person realizes they need God! What a great *day!*

But then what?

Do you see it? The reality is that we need to cling to that mindset – we need to realize we need God every day. Whether we accepted God yesterday or 50 years ago, God wants us to continue to know and understand that we NEED Him. We need God forever *and* in everything we do. We are weak without Him. We cannot effectively complete our spiritual mission on our own human strength or remain in a constant state of spiritual poverty. It's foolish to even consider doing our God-given tasks without Him!

This is the part where, **as believers, we fail.** Somewhere after Day One of accepting Christ into our lives, we've forgotten that we NEED God – even to worship and serve Him!

Many believers are fatigued – even exhausted – while serving God through their God-given purpose or calling. We miss the fact that we need God's help to be capable of serving at our optimum capability. We've been given spiritual gifts, but we're not seeking the Spirit's power to use the gifts at our maximum potential. We are a group of well-intending believers who are unknowingly living in a state of spiritual emptiness and poverty. And we are worn out and exhausted.

This is most visible in our self-care, specifically, our lack of motivation to take care of ourselves.

So, if you're thinking, "I've already given myself to Him completely; that is why I am serving and taking care of others." **And yet you're exhausted,** I have some exciting news. You and I don't have to rely on just our human willpower or the motivational sources in our culture to prepare (or take care of) our bodies so they can be used by God. We have access to the most reliable and powerful source of motivation: The Holy Spirit.

QUICK WORKOUT: PLEASE THINK ABOUT AND ANSWER THE QUESTIONS BELOW.

Do you acknowledge that you need God every day?

_____

_____

_____

How do you think your self-care would change if you invite God into the picture?

_____

_____

_____

Let's pray together. Lord, my desire is to realize my need for You every day. Help me invite you into my self-care daily so I serve when I am prompted by the Holy Spirit and know when to rest appropriately.

DAY 2

Accept God's Help for Self-care

When I was 24 years old, I left my family and hometown for the first time. I was a brand-new nurse, ready to take on the world! But, my climb to the mountaintop quickly ended at the bottom of a mound of self-pity. I relocated in early October and had every expectation to go home for the holidays. But the reality of working in a large hospital (with many, *many,* nurses senior to me) abruptly brought me to full-on adult responsibility. It unexpectedly became my first holiday season away from my family and our holiday customs.

I was surprised at how much I missed my family.

To be totally honest, I remember that Christmas season as my loneliest one. To compensate for my misery, I made our traditional holiday foods and bought the 'special' seasonal candy that I remembered from my childhood. I must say the family holiday foods made me feel better. My needs were met. Not the way I had hoped, but they were met, nonetheless.

My family holiday food strategy worked so well that first season that I continued to do it for all of the major holidays that I worked over the next year. And then, holiday food and candy became the way I spent each holiday away from home. By this point my holiday food and candy solution had spread to minor holidays. And eventually to weekends. And then it became a way of coping in everyday life. My coping pattern continued for over ten years – even after I got married.

Not because I was unhappy; it was just my habit. My bad self-care habits.

I spent years coping with life's stresses and trials using candy or holiday foods to make me feel better emotionally. I've already shared a little about this with you earlier. You see, I had stashes of candy all over my house – it was all about convenience and quick relief. My active lifestyle allowed me to eat this way for a while before I would have to abstain or cut back to lose five to ten pounds that I would have gained. This story may be a shock to people who know me personally because I never looked like I needed to lose weight.

But the truth is, I didn't feel well most days. I had several cavities. And, eventually, my lab values reflected my way of coping. I had high cholesterol in my early thirties (I learned the hard way that a high-sugar diet can cause your cholesterol to rise).

Eventually came those dreaded words, "Lifestyle change."

Somewhere in the middle of all of this, a friend started talking to me about Jesus. I remembered what I learned about Christ as a child and I knew He could 'fix me.' I started working on my relationship with Him for that reason. I was tired of hurting emotionally. But I couldn't *find* the answers to my emotional eating problem anywhere in Scripture.

My prayers to heal my ache *felt* unanswered. I couldn't understand why I wasn't able to *stop* my behavior, either. Then, on a wearying day, I was looking through my massive candy stash when I angrily looked up and shouted, "Jesus, why don't you stop me from eating this candy?!"

The silence was deafening.

But then, "I want you to *want ME*!" was my immediate thought.

And then I knew what I had to change. I brought Christ into my self-care and my journey for self-care freedom began. But I still had ways to go to find freedom from *my bondage*.

My problem was I was 'living in the gray.' I think of 'living in the gray' as a place where I, as a believer, lived in a way that was not completely without any of God's blessings, but I was also not receiving all of God's blessings. I was a believer who sought God's blessing for some parts of my life, but not for the maintenance of my life.

I think it's easy for people like us, people who have a spiritual gift of serving, to live in the gray. We tend to be go-getters. I might say we're type A personality people. So, I think it can happen after we've offered our bodies to God as a living sacrifice, but have not asked, or are not accepting God's blessings related to our self-care. But we need God's blessing, so **we can take care of ourselves in a way that we can be fully capable of carrying out our God-given missions.**

We are the believers who have boldly and courageously said, "Use my body, God," and we're doing it. We're actively serving others with every ounce of our mind and body as a way to worship God. Our mind has been renewed and we've changed our behavior, and we are fully serving God.

But we are only using our human strength, wisdom, and will-power. So, we're struggling to take care of ourselves *and* serve or take care of others.

It can be seen everywhere – and it's interfering with the wellness of believers. People living in the gray are pushing themselves. Pushing until they're in a state of burnout. The worst part about it all is that God's followers are *choosing* to live this way. The reality is: it's <u>a choice</u> to starve our spirit from God's nourishment. And that's the choice we make when we don't live poor (humble) in spirit and decide we don't need God or never consider that we need His help with our self-care.

God continuously offers us nourishment. The word 'nourish' is defined as 'to sustain with food or nutriment; supply with what is necessary for life, health, and growth.'[33] We can always obtain substance from God through worship, prayer, hearing God's word, yielding to the Holy Spirit, fellowship, studying God's word, listening to sermons, and using our gifts, just to name a few. But we must accept it.

Observe a partial list of synonyms for poverty:

- Privation
- Neediness
- Destitution
- Indigence
- Pauperism
- Penury
- Insufficiency
- Thinness
- Inadequacy

- Sparseness
- Shortage

All of these words are defined as an absence of something that is a real need for sustenance. Why would any Christian purposely choose to live and serve in these conditions? I'm not sure, but this is exactly where we camp when we choose to allow our own desires and ways to drive how we take care of ourselves, even when we say we want to live and serve the Lord.

Let's go back to Romans 12:3 again. Remember how earlier I said that Paul speaks about the topic of humility and, in particular, toward the use of our spiritual gifts and our need to be humble and to have faith?

> *For by the grace given me I say to every one of you: Do not think of yourself more highly than you ought, but rather think of yourself with sober judgment, in accordance with the faith God has distributed to each of you* (Romans 12:3).

In addition to being careful not to boast about our spiritual gifts or under-use them, we need to understand that we need God to help us **use them**. God showed me over and over again on my self-care journey that I needed to stop thinking I could take care of myself without Him. This was especially true when I used my gift of service. I was not using sober judgment when I ignored my body's need for rest. I still struggle with the problem of knowing when to rest, and I dare say I think this is the most common way those of us with the gift of service abuse our gift.

QUICK WORKOUT: PLEASE THINK ABOUT AND ANSWER THE QUESTIONS BELOW.

Can you think of a time where you've asked for God's help with your self-care?

_____

_____

_____

Who benefits from believers living in a constant state of poverty of the spirit?

_____

_____

_____

Spend a few minutes in prayer.

DAY 3

How to Stay Focused on God for Self-care

Living as a holy sacrifice is an active and *permanent submission* to God. It's going all in and saying once and for all, "Here is my body, God. I am willing to use it, however way You choose." It's the end of conforming to this world and the beginning of the renewing of your mind and your transformation.

Going 'all in' and giving ourselves completely to God requires *our bodies to be prepared to be used completely for God, too.* Allowing God to help us with our self-care gives us the strength we need to take care of ourselves. God will fortify us, so we are able to do the things we need to do to serve Him at our greatest capacity. The Lord helps us to say, Yes, to the right things and, No, to the wrong things.

Our culture wants us to find respite and strength in our own efforts. Because you're all in for God as a living sacrifice, staying focused on Him is the way to find proper rest.

God's Word helps us separate Christian thinking and human or worldly thinking. When we think we don't need God, we not only miss out on God's many, many promises but we interfere with the self-care motivation and rest God can give us. I buy into this 100%, but I have to admit my satisfaction quickly strays. I'm pretty confident yours does, too. Thankfully, God gives us a way to stay focused, as well as a reliable power source to help us. We can use prayer, gratitude and prayer requests to help us be in constant praise and remembrance.

One verse I like to use for prayer is Psalms 103:1-5. It's a psalm of praise and complete commitment to the Lord:

> *Praise the Lord, my soul; all my inmost being, praise his holy name. Praise the Lord, my soul, and forget not all his benefits – who forgives all your sins and heals all your diseases, who redeems your life from the pit and crowns you with love and compassion, who satisfies your desires with good things so that your youth is renewed like the eagle's.*

One commentator, Warren Wiersbe, pointed out that David uses this verse to show <u>complete focus</u> on the Lord with everything that he is (heart, soul, mind, strength) as he praises and glorifies God. This is pleasing to the Lord. And it is David's intent to obey all of the Lord's commands when he finishes by praising God.[34]

Wiersbe points out that here are six blessings listed in this verse, all familiar to David, and, honestly, all familiar to us:

- Forgiveness
- Healing
- Redemption
- Love
- Satisfaction
- Renewal

Two ways we can fully focus on the Lord and remind ourselves why we need God are praising God and remembering what He has done for us:

- He has been forgiving and merciful of our sins.
- He has healed our sick hearts.
- He has redeemed us from the pit of hell.
- His love is matchless.
- We are satisfied when He fulfills our needs and desires.
- We are renewed when He strengthens us to soar.

QUICK WORKOUT: PLEASE THINK ABOUT AND ANSWER THE QUESTIONS BELOW.

At what times do you notice your satisfaction strays from God?

_____

_____

_____

Take a few moments for prayer. Of the two ways: praising God and remembering what God has done for you, which do you feel will be more helpful to keep your focus?

_____

_____

_____

DAY 4

Maintain Self-care Victory through Faith

Another common strategy of the enemy is to work to weaken our faith. I suspect we all can give examples where we've dealt with this very thing. We've all fallen at least once for twisted truths and lies. But what is important for us as Christians to understand is that Satan *knows* he can never undo our salvation, and he *doesn't try to do so.*

He goes at us through a different angle. Arthur Unger, author of *What Demons Can Do To Saints* writes, "Our enemy strives to convince the Christian that God will never forgive him and their life and testimony are ruined…In fact, Scripture makes its appeal to the believer for a holy walk in God's will on the basis of the fact that the Spirit permanently indwells him and that his salvation is unforfeitably sure."[35]

It's imperative to understand that we, as believers, are secure in our reward of salvation. It can <u>never</u> be removed or taken away from us. It's written clearly in John 14:16, "*And I will ask the Father, and he will give you another advocate to help you and be with you forever…*" Furthermore, even when we sin, or quench the Spirit through our disobedience (1 Thessalonians 5:19), the Holy Spirit is <u>never</u> extinguished.

However, *insecurity about our salvation* interferes with our ability to be strong in the Lord's mighty power[36] (Ephesians 6:10). This never occurred to me as a new believer. I had a basic understanding of my salvation, but I didn't comprehend the Lord's power — or, more importantly, how to use it.

It was only after spending time in the Word did, I appreciate and utilize the power of God against temptation. In order to put on the whole armor of God, I had to understand that the strength and authority over the temptation (or the enemy) came from the Lord, not in my efforts or my length of time as a believer. In other words, as long as I believed the strength to overcome whatever temptation the enemy threw at me came from *me* and not the Lord, I was fighting in my own strength. Without the armor of God, the enemy would take any area of myself that I allowed.

On the other hand, when I learned that victory over Satan comes through *my faith* in God's strength and power, I discovered how to overcome, and sometimes even prevent attacks on my mind, will, emotions and my human tendencies (Galatians 5:19-23).

Romans 6:11 describes our position in the Lord once we are saved. We are dead to sin! Therefore, when we heed Paul's advice and stand firm in our position of faith against the enemy, we can have victory over temptation or spiritual attacks.

Furthermore, when we do fall to temptation, as Christians, we can still experience victory. Our sin doesn't affect our salvation or our standing with God. That said, sin does affect our relationship with Him. Therefore, we must confess our sins to restore our fellowship with the Lord. In fellowship, we are provided God's forgiveness and promises. If we delay or refuse confession, we expose ourselves to ongoing attacks.[37]

I am thankful that attending church helps me to see 'where I am' in my fellowship with God. While the enemy would like me to think my broken fellowship with God affects my salvation – it doesn't. I know this because I hear the truth in church through sermons and worship, and I read it in Scripture. Staying in the Word, and attending church reminds me to confess my sins to God. My repentance and confession restore my fellowship with God. My faith helps me remember what is true in Scripture.

It is so easy to forget. It's easy to get pulled away from the Word – there is always a distraction or interruption. Don't let yourself get pulled away. No matter where you are on your faith journey with Christ, build discipline to be in the Word every day. Strengthen your faith; strengthen your position in the Lord.

QUICK WORKOUT: PLEASE THINK ABOUT AND ANSWER THE QUESTION BELOW.

In what ways have the enemy's lies or twisted truths made you doubt your salvation?

_____

_____

_____

Romans 6:11 reads, *"In the same way, count yourselves dead to sin but alive to God in Christ Jesus."*

Spend some time in prayer and repentance to restore your fellowship with God. I've listed a few of the verses I like to read to prepare my heart for repentance.

"Whoever conceals their sins does not prosper, but the one who confesses and renounces them finds mercy" (Proverbs 28:13).

"If I had cherished sin in my heart, the Lord would not have listened..." (Psalm 66:18).

"Search me, God, and know my heart; test me and know my anxious thoughts. See if there is any offensive way in me, and lead me in the way everlasting" (Psalm 139: 23-24).

Spend time in repentance today and *daily* to maintain fellowship with God and to make faith-driven self-care a priority. Schedule a few minutes on your calendar now.

DAY 5

Use Faith to Live Mission-Capable

Sometimes the best way to explain what something is, is to say what it absolutely isn't. We all know of at least one devoted Christian, maybe even a pastor, who has been diagnosed with cancer or another terminal disease. We also know people who were zealous for health and wellness through persistent healthy eating and committed exercise, and yet died at a young age. Living as a holy sacrifice does not overrule God's will. God knows the number of our days. But the converse is truer: not living as a holy sacrifice does warrant poor health or untimely death because of 'sin.'

Please do not hear me say someone isn't living 'Christian enough' or improperly believe I have a legalistic method of Christian self-care. I pray you understand that is not what I'm saying to you. I'm not asking you to offer your body as a holy sacrifice because I think it will guarantee you will live longer or because I think it will help you prevent cancer or make you a less sinful person.

I'm saying this for one reason.

I'm saying offering your body as a holy sacrifice is an act of worship to honor and please God. The reason why you should offer your body as a living sacrifice to God is because He gave you mercy for your sins through Christ's blood. And, I'm also saying that using your body for God includes how you take care of yourself. When you yield your human willpower to the self-control of the Holy Spirit, you have a powerful source to help you overcome the struggles you experience related to performing your self-care at the capacity required to serve the Lord. You do this by using your body and your spiritual gifts at your greatest ability.

Just relying on our personal (human) desires can have both immediate and long-term consequences. Thinking a certain unhealthy action is acceptable because it's 'trendy,' or 'feels' or 'tastes good,' or 'I like it,' or 'it makes us happy/less lonely/less bored' will only lead to havoc, never wellness. Why? Because we are created in the image of God, never our own. Making decisions through the Holy Spirit will help us live out our purpose. We will never be well when we make decisions that are grounded in selfish pleasure.

WHEN WE ARE CHOOSEY

The world tells us we should take care of ourselves out of:

- Fear (to prevent obesity, cancer or heart disease)
- Pride (we need our sex appeal and we should feel happy and good always)
- Pressure (to look young, to match a social icon)
- General social expectations (so we look healthy)
- Willpower (we are capable of doing so completely on our own)

There are also worldly barriers preventing us from doing these things including:

- Time
- Money

- Cravings and addictions (created by habits and food companies)
- Incorrect information
- Our brokenness, our emotions, our fears and failures... being human

You may be aware that fear, pressure and willpower have been proven to be ineffective. On the flip side God tells us to avoid conforming to social expectations or being prideful. I think this shows us that our motives and reasons are not enough. Our own reasons for taking care of ourselves are never going to be enough to keep our self-care at an appropriate level. What is enough? Doing it for God's glory and His mission.

But, somehow, even with the barriers, the worldly reasons seem less intimidating and we try to take it on by ourselves. Why is it that we prefer our way instead of the right way?

We like to think we can be open to receiving instructions. But, if we're being truly honest, if it is uncomfortable or if it feels restrictive...we like it best if it is our way. And we grumble when things change, and we can't control it. We sound like the Israelites in the wilderness!

You may be thinking what I thought. "I know why I don't always see total dependence on God in me. I don't *have* to rely on God for manna, water and quail like the Israelites did because I can fend for myself. In fact, unless I make a point to spend time with God, sometimes I don't even feel like I *need* Him."

No, the problem isn't that we don't have to rely on God for food or that our physical needs are so filled that we don't need Him. It is because we want to pick and choose what we need from God regardless of His plan.

Because when it comes down to it, we don't trust His plan for us. And that's why we choose the worldly way. When we do this, we miss out on the very foundational nourishment God wants to provide for us. How much simpler to trust God's plan, and embrace the humility of living as a holy sacrifice as a way to worship God!

Talk about motivational sources. When you are tired and worn out from serving and taking care of others, when you have other options, that's when you want to eat the sugary foods that you know are not good for you.

QUICK WORKOUT: PLEASE THINK ABOUT AND ANSWER THE QUESTIONS BELOW.

What worldly barriers prevent you from taking care of your body in a way that can make you mission-capable?

_____

_____

_____

Which method is the easier way to be mission-capable? The way culture recommends, or the way Scripture commands? Explain.

_____

_____

_____

Let's pray. Father, I do not want to spend another moment following the promptings of my culture. I want to be nourished by your promises. I pray I can live my life and take care of myself in a way that is honoring and pleasing to You.

A Promise from God

Pastor and author Bill Hybels in his book *The Power of a Whisper* wrote, "In John 8:44, Jesus calls Satan the 'father of lies.' At every turn, the ultimate fraud will try to convince you that peace is not available, that temptation is not escapable and that God's grace is only a temporary gift. God's truth must dwell so deeply in us that we can conquer the evil one's lies."[38]

We must stay in the Word to know God's truth. And we must let God fortify our mission and serving efforts.

Every day, we are in a battle against our own human desires, and only with humility can we choose the path of the Spirit. We have to make the choice for humility at each decision point. In each moment a decision arrives.

Our selfish desires create tension, which makes yielding to the Spirit a lot more complicated than we'd like it to be. On any given day, we want to eat food that is healthy, but we also want it to taste deliciously sweet or salty, give us bounding energy (caffeine), be available at our convenience, and at a low cost, too.

God has given us a part of Himself with the intent to guide us through all of our decisions. In order for that to happen we have to decide not to do what our mind or body is loudly telling us to do and, instead, yield to the Holy Spirit's way.

Have nothing to do with godless myths and old wives' tales;
rather, train yourself to be godly. For physical training is
of some value, but godliness has value for all things,

holding promise for both the present life and the life to come. This is a trustworthy saying that deserves full acceptance. That is why we labor and strive, because we have put our hope in the living God, who is the Savior of all people, and especially of those who believe (1 Timothy 4:7-10).

QUICK WORKOUT: PLEASE THINK ABOUT AND ANSWER THE QUESTIONS BELOW.

Spend several moments in prayer today. What do you need to do to ensure you do not live in a state of spiritual poverty?

_____

_____

_____

Why do you need to ask God to help you with your self-care?

_____

_____

_____

RECAP

How do you apply faith to your self-care?

- Admit You Need God
- Accept God's Help
- Stay Focused on God
- Find Victory through Faith
- Live Mission-Capable

To apply living as a holy sacrifice to your self-care, you need to humbly admit that you need God. Specifically, you need God to help you with your self-care.

My challenge to you is two-fold. First, admit that you truly need God. Next, accept God's help – especially in regard to your self-care.

And, accept the strength and power of the Holy Spirit when you use your spiritual gift.

Chapter 5

Overcome Self-care Temptations

Any chance you've been car shopping lately?

Have you ever noticed how something weird happens right after you narrow your search to a specific make and model? New or used – it doesn't matter! As soon as your choice is made, suddenly you see what seems like hundreds of that same make and model out and about all around you. It's like all of a sudden, everyone is already driving the very car you want!

That's not what happened, of course. The reality is that they've been there the whole time; it's just that you've never noticed them. They've been completely invisible until your decision was made and it became an area of focus for you.

This phenomenon also occurs when you decide to sell your home. Almost instantaneously, your once comfortable and perfectly acceptable surroundings are screaming for attention, repairs, and updating. You are suddenly painfully aware of the hours and hours of work that are ahead of you, which just minutes ago were completely unseen.

With nothing changing except your intent – you see a totally different reality.

Another time when the reality is hidden is when we're trying to win an argument with someone or prove that we are right. I can think of numerous times when my desire to be right in a discussion blinded me from the accuracy and validity of the facts, that is, until my motive changed. Just like in the car and house examples above, once I changed my intent, I saw the truth of the situation – which didn't just suddenly change – it was always that way!

So, as you might expect, when I give up my desire to do things my way (through pride) to be obedient to God (through humility), I see a different reality. It's always been there but I was blind to it until my obedience became my intent or focus. When we want to be right (or do things our way) we can't see how to make godly, or righteous, choices. Why? Because God's choices don't fit into *our intent* – so we don't see or recognize them.

Our pride can blind us from what God has saved us to see.

Obviously, not seeing God's path causes us to go on the only other path, which is sin. And, sometimes, as we discussed in the last chapter, our pride can take us so far off of God's path that we end up in a state of spiritual poverty, incomplete wellness, and even illness.

I gave an example of when this happened to me; I experienced loneliness but, instead of calling out to God (and seeing or acknowledging the loneliness), I fixed my problem my way and calmed my hurt emotions by eating holiday food and candy.

But I've discovered something amazing on this journey. Offering our body as a living sacrifice out of obedience to God, *helps us* avoid committing sin to and with our body!

Our *intent* to obey is the catalyst for overcoming self-care related temptations.

I'll warn you. You're probably going to experience a period where 'the blinders fall off' – much like when you pick out a new car or decide to sell your home. And, let me tell you, it is more than humbling when that happens! It may take you on a rollercoaster of emotions as you allow your will and independence with your body to be destroyed.

However, it's also an incredible period for spiritual strength and growth. I learned how to overcome my self-care temptations during this time.

Now, I am thankful for the experience. And, I want that for you, too, so that's where we're going next.

So, buckle up and get ready for the ride!

How to Overcome Self-care Temptation

DAY 1

Yield All Parts of Your Life to the Spirit

One of the reasons I felt led to write this book is because of the large number of patients who have crossed my path. Most deeply *wanted* to do the things that would make or keep them well. Many actually thought they were doing the right things, only to discover, they weren't. And, many, many just *couldn't* do the right things.

Why?

Why is it that intelligent, purposeful people, and even highly devoted Christians just cannot stay on track to provide themselves with good self-care? I just can't stop asking myself this question. "Why can't people take better care of themselves? What motivational source do they lack?" In a world where clinical research has shown positive health outcomes can come through the use of meditation and mindfulness, could it be they lack *these* things?

Or is it weak – or lack of – willpower?

What on earth is missing?

And then I keep coming back to the question that makes me uncomfortable, the question that causes me to expect judgment from others. The question that delayed me writing this book – out of fear for thinking of this question:

Could the poor self-care performance of our sisters and brothers in Christ be the work of our enemy?

One of the biggest reasons I'm uncomfortable asking this question is because I didn't want to dig into the answer. Dealing with a spiritual enemy doesn't seem like something I want to mess with.

But, thankfully, Merrill Unger, author of *What Demons Can Do To Saints* provides a wealth of knowledge, and deeper insight into how our enemy derails, among other things, our self-care. I read, reread, underlined, researched, and studied his book. I discovered that the answer to my question is Yes...but not how I thought it was occurring.

As a believer, I hope you know that God offers you eternal hope through salvation; Christ's death on the cross was for you. But God also assists us with our struggles on earth because the Holy Spirit, who lives within us after we proclaim Christ is Lord, fends off the attacks of our enemy.

To help me explain the answer to my main question, we have to first understand some answers to some other questions. Please know, these questions are nothing more than questions that I asked during my prayer-time and along my journey. These are not based on anything more than thoughts that came to me (in other words, these are not influenced by a theologian's philosophy or commentary).

The first question is: "When we struggle with food or other self-care related temptations, is our enemy fighting with the Spirit within us?"

We can find the answer to my first question in Unger's book where he writes that the "internal struggle of the believer is revealed to be a **warfare between the Spirit and the flesh**, not between the Holy Spirit and demon spirits…The Christian has the full equipment to conduct a successful warfare against the enemy (Ephesians 6:11-18), and the armor provided is for **external**, not internal foes"[39] (Romans 6:1-7:25; Galatians 5:17, emphasis added).

Unger goes on to make this amazing statement, "The experience of salvation furnishes no *magical* protection against Satan…. Salvation, however, does provide *miraculous* protection (God working supernaturally). And what a difference there is between the two!"[40]

Okay. Our struggle with food or other self-care temptations is related to our own flesh – not Satan. It's based on our own desires, our intent. This answer is like the new car example I gave. When we need help with our self-care struggles, we need to change our intent (from our way to God's way), so we can call on the strength and power of the Holy Spirit within us. We can then tap into the Holy Spirit's self-control, faithfulness and forbearance, among other fruit of the Spirit.

The second question is: "When we struggle with food or other self-care related temptations, can our body be invaded by the enemy?" And then I also wondered, "If I don't yield my self-care to the Holy Spirit, can the enemy interfere with our self-care?"

First of all, Unger believes that neither Satan nor his demons can dwell in our bodies when the Holy Spirit does.[41] That said, the enemy may have opportunities to tempt us which answers the second part of my question. One reason is because we can yield just some parts of our lives to the Lord, *and yet still keep many parts of our lives unyielded.* Therefore, although it may seem a little like splitting hairs, this response begs the question, "Have I completely yielded my body and my self-care to the Holy Spirit?" Yielding your body and self-care to the Holy Spirit will help you avoid or overcome temptations related to your body or self-care, and it prevents the enemy from having any influence over you.

Merrill's answer led me to the obvious third question: "What if our self-care is not yielded to the Spirit?"

Unger writes, "If the believer is not controlled by the Holy Spirit, he will be dominated by the flesh, which shows...a close affinity with the powers of darkness." And sins of the flesh are not the only way to invite attack from our enemy; "sins of the spirit, notably pride and self-righteousness, do the same."[42] Satan operates through that part of the flesh that has not died to our old way of living, and to that degree can gain control of our lives through our old nature (See Ephesians 2:2).

So what's the final answer to my third question? What happens when a Christian fails to yield their self-care (or any other part of a Christian's life) to the Holy Spirit? The answer is the believer's attempt at self-care (or whatever part of a Christian's life) that is not yielded to the Holy Spirit, <u>can be overwhelmed by pressures from their own fleshly desires and struggles</u>.

It's literally a war within ourselves, which tells me there are a lot of people who have internal wars going on.

This answer makes me think about what happens with _my_ self-care when I'm in a bad mood or have a bad day.

Is it great? No, it's definitely not great.

And, what about the days I don't have the mental energy to summon up my willpower?

My self-care suffers. And I bet it does for you, too.

What should we do? Are you thinking we can probably handle it if we try harder? Work on our willpower?

I don't think that's a successful way.

Because the final answer to my original question, "Could the poor self-care performance of our sisters and brothers in Christ be the work of our enemy?" is a little bit complex.

The bottom line is that, although our struggles are not directly from the enemy, they are being driven by the manipulation of the desires (intent) of our own body (or flesh). So, when you ask, "Well, is this _really_ that big of a deal? I mean, how bad can our flesh be on our self-care performance?"

You need to understand the answer is absolutely yes! It's a major problem! Because Galatians 5:17-21 shows us the intent of our flesh,

For the flesh desires what is contrary to the Spirit, and the Spirit what is contrary to the flesh. They are in conflict with each other, so that you are not to do whatever you want. But if you are led by the Spirit, you are not under the law. The acts of the flesh are obvious: sexual immorality, impurity, and debauchery; idolatry and witchcraft, hatred, discord, jealousy, fits of rage, selfish ambition, dissensions, factions and envy; drunkenness, orgies, and the like. I warn you, as I did before, that those who live like this will not inherit the kingdom of God.

Our flesh *desires* doing things our own way. **These internal desires come out as behaviors.**

- They come out as choosing convenience over quality food.
- They come out as picking the sweet or salty food over the fruit and vegetables.
- They come out as saying you have freedom from 'a diet.'
- They come out as picking food to soothe or comfort our emotions, focusing only on inexpensive food, and caffeine, alcohol and so on.

In short, they come out as these self-care behaviors. But the desires relate back to jealousy, debauchery, selfish ambition, envy, and other works of the flesh.

There is a solution to this problem!

The solution is in Galatians 5:25: "*Since we are living by the Spirit, let us follow the Spirit's leading in every part of our lives.*" Yielding <u>all</u>

parts of your life, *including your self-care,* to the Spirit allows the Holy Spirit – and not your fleshly desires – to drive your self-care decisions and actions. Living as a holy sacrifice is an *active* way to abandon flesh-driven self-care and move towards faith-driven self-care.

But let me be clear here; this doesn't happen overnight.

And it may not happen without outside assistance (treatment by a healthcare provider, mental health counseling or therapy, a weight-loss group, medications, budgeting classes, talking to pastor, etc.). Our desires are formed and shaped by our life's experiences. So, I cannot let you read this and set up a Pollyanna-like optimism.

It's still going to take work. But with an obedient and humble intent, and with your eyes on the Lord, you can begin to single out your behaviors. That allows you to start identifying and linking self-care behaviors to your desires, so you know where to start working.

For a few of you, just realizing this truth will help you take better care of yourself.

But for many others, it will take spending time in the Word, and spending time in prayer with the Lord. It may take some Bible journaling, reading Scripture, maybe a related devotional every morning, working through a self-care action plan, or maybe even learning more about what God wants you to do with your life.

This is how I learned how to overcome self-care temptations.

Yes, it takes work, but you'll see how to take better care of yourself, and you'll be motivated to do so!

QUICK WORKOUT: PLEASE THINK ABOUT AND ANSWER THE QUESTIONS BELOW.

What is something you know you do because your flesh is driving your self-care decisions?

_____

_____

_____

What is something you know you don't do your flesh is driving your self-care decisions?

_____

_____

_____

Spend a few moments in reflective prayer. Do you need to yield all of your self-care to the Spirit?

_____

_____

_____

DAY 2

Identify Your Idols

Whether we think so or not, we all have idols. I know of at least one of mine. Maybe this one is yours, too?

Do you like the feeling of being in control of, well, everything?

In addition to overcoming emotional eating and poor self-care, I am a partially reformed control-freak (I gave the Lord a lot to work with upfront!). I can't say I'm fully reformed yet. I still race out of the gate bound and determined to control whatever problem is facing me at the moment or threatening me on that day.

I tend to plan scenarios in my head – one after another – until I have so many in my mind that they start to crowd each other and even have to sit on top of each other. I'm not satisfied until I've tried to think of a scenario for every possible angle. I wonder if the multiple scenarios stored in my mind, having to wait in piles, all squished together to somehow send a signal to me. The word 'signal' is of course a euphemism for anxiety, stress and a horrible headache.

You see, that's usually the point when I remember that I am not in control, I've never been in control, and I'm not even supposed to try to be in control. I will gladly tell you that I am submitting control to the Lord sooner than I used to. But maybe, like you, I still have some work to do – because I frequently still *want to be in control.*

That's how it works with our idols, we *want* something. We truly *desire* them. And that desire may not ever go away!

I want to go pretty deep into this. Of course, we can't talk about every single idol here, so I'll share the details about mine and you can think about one of yours along the same lines throughout this section.

When I want to have control, I'm essentially deciding that I can handle the situation better than God. And, when I 'take' control, guess what? I tap into other idols. I become less patient. And greedier. Unfortunately, when I'm trying to be in control *and also* impatient and greedy, I usually experience an increase of some 'great ideas' – which are nothing but foolish or ungodly thoughts. Imagine me saying, "Hold my chai tea!" and jumping into something headfirst doing it my way – with no regard at all to God's way. Let me tell you, those schemes always crash and burn.

Do you find this happening to you, too? Well, there's a good explanation. When we decide to be 'in-control,' we are actually deciding to live 'out-of-control.' This is especially true when it comes to our self-care. Why? Because we lose our 'standard.' And, without a standard, there is no control to center us. When we take our focus off God and focus on our human will, we have to set our own standards.

Know what? That's the very definition of idolatry. Idolatry, in the Christian faith, is defined as anything that we replace for the one, true God. Our standard. When I yield my self-care to the Spirit, it becomes obvious to me that my notions are ungodly, with even worse consequences.

In the Old Testament, idols were portrayed mostly as blocks of wood or stone. In the New Testament, idolatry was connected to covetousness. Paul describes the origin of idolatry in Romans 1:21-25. Today, we have a variety of idols, and they're numerous but the majority of our idols are related to heart-matters. Today's forms of idolatry tend to center on our pride, self-centeredness, greed, gluttony, a love for possessions and, ultimately, our *desire* to rebel against our one true God.

What's important is that we don't want to do these things when we acknowledge God's love and mercy, stay in the Word, fellowship with God in prayer, and obediently take care of ourselves as a form of worship to Him.

But, when we close the Bible, stop our prayers, go AWOL during fellowship times, forget about God's love and mercy, and start trying to do things based on our desires or our own thinking, we get into trouble pretty fast. Of course, when we go this route, we think we'll be okay because we have our willpower, we're strong, and we know how to find the right 'mental energy.' Moreover, we have access to appropriate help in our culture and we don't need God for things like this.

What a slippery slope!

Just One Time!

When it comes to our self-care, I can't think of a more dangerous lie to say to ourselves than 'It's just this one time.' And, we always kid ourselves!

When we put our focus on our desires (and not God) we can quickly be led to worship other things. The value of convenience, instant gratification, good-tasting food, or general pleasure for ourselves are just a few examples of things that seem more important to us than pleasing God. When we make decisions about our self-care with the mental attitude of 'I can do it this one time,' we are more easily led to an ungodly lifestyle.

For a Christian, that can mean living in a state of spiritual poverty. Eventually, we can even forget how to do math. We apply our selfish attitude to *multiple* decisions in a day until we are ultimately living a life of complete self-care **rebellion**.

Here is an illustration of how easy it is for us to slide down the slippery slope – well, it's actually how I used to live:

1. We desire [fill in the blank]. My example, [a healthy body – or the way people will look at me with a healthy body].
2. We tell ourselves, "Okay, this [blank][exercise] is my standard for my self-care activity."
3. Next, we see something we want to eat or do (or maybe even more likely, we see something we don't want to eat or do – like eat a salad or exercise).
4. What do we say to ourselves? Do it anyway? Stick to the plan? Live up to my standards?
5. No, we tell ourselves, I'm really tired (sad, bored, mad, etc.) right now, so it's okay to ignore my standard *this one time*. It's just for today. It's just for this one time.
6. And we do (or don't do) it.
7. And then, we forget how to do math.

8. Somehow, we tell ourselves, "It's okay this one time," the next day. And we do it again.

9. Then the next day comes, we do it again, and again, and again. Our one-time mindset creates an exponential rate of poor choices.

10. The rebellion to our own original desire becomes our new standard. Our habit. Our way of life.

So, in my illustration above, first, we desire one thing (healthy body and maybe attention), then, we desire another (control, freedom, or even negative emotions). <u>First, we desire, then we desire again!</u>

The truth is, when we turn away from God, *we* are never in control. Our *desires* are. Plus, our desires change. In addition, some of our desires are stronger than others (especially the subconscious ones). And, remember, our fleshly desires are *always* contrary to the desires of the Spirit.

Our willpower cannot overpower the desires of our flesh.

Robert Strand, author of *Self-Control Nine Fruits of the Spirit, A Devotion Series,* offers some insight into how the Holy Spirit can help us. The Holy Spirit is the producer of the fruit of self-control. When the Spirit is in control, we have the power to lead our self-care towards the care that is at God's higher and absolute standard.

Strand compares the word 'self-control,' to its Greek source 'enkrateia' where 'en' means to be infused or within, and 'kratos' represents 'vigor,'' dominion,' 'power,' 'strength.' The overall meaning is 'a great force within but under control.' Strand goes on to say "Self-control plays a major role in the maturing of the other fruit in our living. This one provides what is needed to make the other eight operational. Self-control is the glue which holds all of life and all of the harvest of the fruit of the Spirit...Self-control in reality is a very high form of worship because it is a living out of His commandments – it's a 'doing' acts of character in order that all of the fruit of the Spirit will be seen in us."[43]

In short, self-control helps us recognize God's love and mercy, and gives us the supernatural power needed to provide the best self-care to our body (and give our best to our church). As believers, we get the privilege to have the ability to manifest self-control; it is God's way to make us more like Jesus.[43] It helps us overcome our temptations and helps us identify and then free us from falling to our desired idols.

It should be no surprise that our enemy would most readily go after the character that acts as the hinge pin to the rest of the fruit of the Spirit.

QUICK WORKOUT: PLEASE THINK ABOUT AND ANSWER THE QUESTIONS BELOW.

If the majority of our idols are related to heart matters, what are the idols in your life?

_____

_____

_____

How has worshiping your idol(s) affected your recent self-care activity?

_____

_____

_____

Let's pray. Lord, I am always humbled and saddened by the number of idols in my life. They are invisible to me unless I turn my focus back to you. My prayer is that I turn back to you so I can benefit from the fruit of the Spirit and avoid the familiar temptation of worshipping my idols.

DAY 3

Smash Your Idols through Prayer

Before you can fully overcome self-care temptations, you need to identify, and then 'smash' your idols.

In addition to our flesh interfering with our self-care, our enemy attacks the health and wellness of the church by tempting us, *individually*, by drawing us away from living by the Spirit and back into living in our fleshly ways. I'll talk more about this in the next chapter. The enemy also tries to tempt us individually when we experience physical, mental or emotional symptoms. He tries to lure us away from focusing on God by getting us to give in to the desires of our flesh when we are most weak and vulnerable. This strategy can and DOES affect our self-care.

In fact, we saw the enemy tempt Jesus in this way in Matthew 4:1-11.

Then Jesus was led by the Spirit into the wilderness to be tempted by the devil. After fasting forty days and forty nights, he was hungry. The tempter came to him and said, 'If you are the Son of God, tell these stones to become bread.'

Jesus answered, "It is written, 'Man shall not live on bread alone, but on every word that comes from the mouth of God.'"

Then the devil took him to the holy city and had him stand on the highest point of the temple. "If you are the Son of God," he said, "throw yourself down. For it is written: 'He will command his angels concerning you, and they will lift you up in their hands, so that you will not strike your foot again a stone.'"

Jesus answered him, "It is also written: 'Do not put the Lord your God to the test.'"

Again, the devil took him to a very high mountain and showed him all the kingdoms of the world and their splendor. "All this I will give you," he said, "if you will bow down and worship me."

Jesus said to him, "Away from me, Satan! For it is written: 'Worship the Lord your God, and serve him only.'"

Then the devil left him, and angels came and attended him.

The devil tempts Jesus in the areas where he thinks Jesus as Man is the most vulnerable. He starts by tempting Jesus with food because of his physical hunger. Jesus responds with Scripture. The devil then tempts Jesus with what he thinks will inspire selfish ambitions – by urging Jesus to work miracles that were not instructed by the Father. Finally, the devil tempts the patience and obedience of Jesus by tempting Jesus to claim His kingdom than the designated time.

How did Jesus overcome these temptations?

In all cases, Jesus uses the Bible to resist Satan's temptations in this combat. It is through the power of the Holy Spirit that Jesus rejects Satan's urgings to perform spectacular signs at his bidding. On the other hand, Jesus performs mighty miracles such as the feeding of the 5,000 and raising of the dead at the will of the Father.

Our enemy can easily tempt us to lean on our own strength when we have physical or mental/emotional symptoms or weakness. In my opinion, the greatest lie our enemy uses to trick us relating to our symptoms and our self-care is with the temptation of thinking we can be in control. There are many worldly options that can 'help' you take control of your diet, self-care, disease, etc. And, no doubt, our desire to be in control interferes with our self-care. Think about how often we jump in the driver's seat every time we have a new experience (like a symptom or illness).

But, what does the Bible tell us to do when we develop a symptom or become ill? It instructs us to <u>pray</u>.

The apostle James gives precise instructions regarding our response to our illnesses.

> *Are any of you sick? You should call for the elders of the church to come and pray over you, anointing you with oil in the name of the Lord. Such a prayer offered in faith will heal the sick, and the Lord will make you well. And if you have committed any sins, you will be forgiven* (James 5:14-15) (NLT).[44]

Unfortunately, most of us ignore this command when we first become ill. We allow our human understanding of health and medicine, feelings, cultural norms, our experiences, or our education to drive our initial choices around what we do to find healing.

And we make it complicated. We're confused about what point is the right time to start to pray for healing.

- Is it now?
- Is it before you have an appointment with a doctor?
- Is it after you get a new diagnosis?

Or should it be a little later because:

- Your life is too busy.
- You're serving or taking care of others.
- You don't feel worthy.
- You don't have any motivation.
- You don't believe it will get worse.
- You don't know how to change your lifestyle.
- You don't care.

We don't know our self-care matters to kingdom growth. I've seen this happen over and over and over. Yes, the worst thing I see is that NO ONE CONSIDERS PRAYING when they first become ill. And, we hardly ever pray for our self-care.

We aren't taught to pray about our symptoms for our self-care. But, we can! We can pray right now. We can anytime. We can pray in gratitude and thankfulness for the absence of physical or mental symptoms! We have small groups, life groups, disciple groups – all of these people would be willing to pray. And the elders of the church will pray.

But we don't ask for it. We don't pray when we are free of symptoms and we don't pray when we first get them. And, all the while, the unrestrained tendency to control keeps us locked in a repetitive series of trying to take better care of ourselves but failing, trying again to take better care of ourselves but failing, over and over until we're finally faced with a catastrophic event.

Our lack of prayer for our self-care enables our idols. It affects how we use our spiritual gifts. It interferes with us being a church. And, it pulls our focus away from our overall mission, the Great Commission!

QUICK WORKOUT: PLEASE THINK ABOUT AND ANSWER THE QUESTIONS BELOW.

What idol do you need to smash first?

_____

_____

_____

Prayerfully consider where you can place prayer about your self-care into your day.

_____

_____

_____

DAY 4

God Strengthens Our Weaknesses

We are WIIFM people. 'What's in it for me' is what we all want to know, right? Even sometimes when we read Scripture.

As you were reading the last section, you may have wondered, "Why should I ask for prayer for something so simple? Why should I follow what is written in James and call on an elder for something like this?"

Because "*Such a prayer offered in faith will heal the sick, and the Lord will make you well. And if you have committed any sins, you will be forgiven*" (James 5:15).

A prayer through faith requires that you become humble so that you can turn back to the Lord. When you do this, you are made well in that your sins are forgiven, and you will again be in fellowship with the Lord. And, when you turn away from your own desires, you allow the Spirit to help you with your self-care and give you what you need to resist the temptations that are targeting your self-care.

Of course, this instruction is not just for the people who have physical or emotional symptoms; it is also offered to those who are sick spiritually – especially people who are living in spiritual poverty.

Request for this prayer is what leads to the definition of wellness from the beginning of this book. Here wellness was defined as "*the quality or state* of being healthy in body and mind *especially <u>as the result of a deliberate effort</u>.* God asks that we place our deliberate efforts towards our spiritual <u>worship, in the form of self-care,</u> to find wellness."

It is my mission to encourage Christians to implement this request for prayer, healing, and forgiveness with – and even before – the initial diagnosis of a symptom or ailment (high cholesterol, high blood pressure, being overweight) versus waiting until a terminal or difficult diagnosis manifests. My hope is also that those who desire basic or continued wellness will pray. When we humble ourselves and submit our bodies to the Lord as a holy sacrifice, we have access to the fruit of the Holy Spirit.

But I must clarify that crushing idols and returning to God doesn't always mean you'll have a fairy-tale ending. We don't follow a prosperity gospel. What it does mean is that you have the love and virtues of God, the grace of Christ, and the power of the Spirit to help you on the journey. And this is important to understand because sometimes healing doesn't come right away.

Life as a follower of Jesus is an ongoing battle. Just because you crush an idol and turn back to God doesn't mean that everything wrong with you physically, mentally or emotionally will be instantly fixed. And, it doesn't mean your self-care will suddenly be simple either. We all have places within us where we feel empty, sense a need, or have a longing. We all want to fill the empty space. It's uncomfortable, and the vacancy makes us feel weak.

The point is God specifically created some of our weaknesses and our need for Him. God wants us to turn to Him when we feel empty or weak. But when we identify these needs or weaknesses and choose to fill them in other ways, we leave God out of the equation. As we've been discussing, we sometimes think of other ways to fill our holes or make us feel stronger or better in various situations: these are our idols.

Paul admitted his weakness to the Corinthians:

> *Three times I pleaded with the Lord to take it away from me. But he said to me, "My grace is sufficient for you, for my power is made perfect in weakness." Therefore I will boast all the more gladly about my weaknesses, so that Christ's power may rest on me* (2 Corinthians 12:8-9).

God is faithful and will be there along our journey to provide us with what we need. Most times the love and virtue of God, the grace of Christ or the power of the Spirit help you see that you need more help. There are times when what we need is to go through counseling. Or attend a class to learn how to improve something related to our self-care or resolve something that is interfering with our goals. And, there are times when additional medical services or products are needed. But, if we don't stop filling our needs with our idols, we can't let God strengthen our weaknesses.

QUICK WORKOUT: PLEASE THINK ABOUT AND ANSWER THE QUESTIONS BELOW.

In what areas do you feel weak?

_____

_____

_____

What do you generally do to strengthen those weaknesses? Are you interfering with God's way to strengthen your weaknesses?

_____

_____

_____

Let's pray together. Father, my desire is to allow You to strengthen my weaknesses. I want to stop filling my needs with idols and trust Your faithfulness on this journey.

DAY 5

There is Rest in Obedience

The following story about Daniel is a beautiful example of Daniel's strong faith, the trust he had in God's plan, his obedience, and how he dealt with the challenges of doing something different than the surrounding culture expects.

Daniel did not have access to the indwelling Holy Spirit though the Holy Spirit would come upon him. However, he had faith and hope that God would deliver him, and he was blessed for that.

The first chapter of Daniel is an amazing account of faith, trust, obedience, and blessing. Daniel and his three friends demonstrate their love for God through *life-risking obedience*. God then blesses their efforts, by giving them more than they had hoped for. Their reverence for the Mosaic Law, its dietary laws, in particular, results in observable improvements in their health, and in the wellness of their attitudes and thoughts.

But Daniel resolved not to defile himself with the royal food and wine, and he asked the chief official for permission not to defile himself this way.

Now God had caused the official to show favor and compassion to Daniel, but the official told Daniel, 'I am afraid of my lord the king, who has assigned your food and drink. Why should he see you looking worse than the other young men your age? The king would then have my head because of you.'

Daniel then said to the guard whom the chief official had appointed over Daniel, Hananiah, Mishael and Azariah, "Please test your servants for ten days: Give us nothing but vegetables to eat and water to drink. Then compare our appearance with that of the young men who eat the royal food and treat your servants in accordance with what you see."

So he agreed to this and tested them for ten days. At the end of the ten days they looked healthier and better nourished than any of the young men who ate the royal food.

So the guard took away their choice food and the wine they were to drink and gave them vegetables instead.

To these four young men God gave knowledge and understanding of all kinds of literature and learning. And Daniel could understand visions and dreams of all kinds.

At the end of the time set by the king to bring them into his service, the chief official presented them to Nebuchadnezzar. The king talked with them, and he found none equal to Daniel, Hananiah, Mishael and Azariah; so they entered the king's service.

In every matter of wisdom and understanding about which the king questioned them, he found them ten times better than all the magicians and enchanters in his whole kingdom (Daniel 1:8-20).

Daniel refused to defile himself (be morally and ceremonially impure) with the royal food and wine, due to improperly followed food laws, where the food was inherently unclean, improperly prepared or partly offered to idols. The source of Daniel's obedience was his love and trust in God which allowed him to overcome the barriers in front of him.

The Daniel story is an exemplary picture of personal integrity in a place where there were numerous barriers. It shows, as it is today, that it was not at all easy to adhere to moral or ethical principles. By choosing this way of eating they were not blending in with the others in the palace, nor were they bowing to peer pressure and court protocol where everyone is expected to eat the king's food.

This moral choice requires courage. No one likes to be different – especially when society judges you. But when it is done for the right reasons and the right way – through faith – God's plans can be accomplished. A commitment must be present, and here it is seen through obedience. The point, however, is that their obedience was not out of obligation. It was out of love and reverence.

God wants to bless us for our obedience to Him. And when we do it with our body and/or self-care, He can bless us with spiritual, emotional, or even physical wellness.

QUICK WORKOUT: PLEASE THINK ABOUT AND ANSWER THE QUESTIONS BELOW.

What barriers in your culture prevent you from being committed to your self-care efforts?

_____

_____

_____

Spend a few minutes in quiet reflection. How could faith and obedience to God specifically help you find rest?

_____

_____

_____

A Promise from God

None of God's requests or commands is without some form of benefit to us. His commands are good and protect us without exception. When we offer our bodies, once and for all, as a holy sacrifice, we not only worship God, but have access to the power of the Spirit, which we can use to overcome temptations related to our self-care!

When we are obedient and offer our bodies as a living and holy sacrifice, we gain the strength and endurance of the Spirit and can avoid worshiping idols and committing sin to and with our body.

> *...but those who hope in the Lord will renew their strength. They will soar on wings like eagles; they will run and not grow weary, they will walk and not be faint* (Isaiah 40:31 emphasis added).

QUICK WORKOUT: PLEASE THINK ABOUT AND ANSWER THE QUESTIONS BELOW.

This chapter talks about the many ways temptations interfere with your self-care. How can making the choice to follow the Spirit help you overcome your temptations?

_____

_____

_____

Earlier you identified an idol you wanted to smash. What does the promise in Isaiah 40:31 encourage you to do or change so you can smash your idol?

_____

_____

_____

Let's pray. Father, my desire is to be obedient. I want to offer my body as a living and holy sacrifice. I ask You to help me do this to gain the strength and endurance of the Spirit and avoid worshipping my idols.

RECAP

How do you Overcome Self-care Temptation?

- Yield All of My Life to the Spirit
- Identify my Idols
- Smash my Idols through Prayer
- Let God Strengthen me in my Weaknesses
- Find Rest through Obedience

God knows we have only two choices: to follow the desires of our flesh or follow the Spirit.

We are not asked to spend our time on earth alone. We have the Spirit's self-control (and eight other fruits of the Spirit) to help us. When we exercise self-control, we avoid the dependence on our own strength and willpower, which weakens and tires. And, most importantly, we can contribute to the advancement of God's Church and the Holy Kingdom.

My challenge to you is to yield all areas of your life to the Spirit, identify the idols that are driving your self-care behavior, and smash those idols.

Chapter 6

Revive Body Life

The evening started out like every other evening during our seventh year of marriage. But, that night, we made an amazing discovery.

And it changed everything in our marriage.

While I was taking a roast out of the crockpot, I looked at the meat and cringed. The roast was as tough as old, dried-out shoe leather. I started to explain my frustration to my husband, "I am so done with this crockpot. I was trying to make you roast. I know you like it, but I don't know what I keep doing wrong."

He interrupted my explanation, and his response changed the trajectory of our marriage. "Lisa, I don't like roast. I only eat it because you like it."

I smiled and said, "Honey, I don't like it either!"

And that roast was the last roast I ever made.

This conversation was a turning point for us in our marriage.

We identified a lack of true fellowship between the two of us. Because it was easier to *assume* how the other person felt, we thought we could avoid seemingly tough conversations. The hard conversations are what would have led us to the truth about how each other felt about things, and also true fellowship. Instead, our false perceptions led us to mediocre attempts to accommodate the other.

We were able to laugh it off, but we realized we needed to dig a little deeper and work a little harder to get to enjoy the true fellowship available to us in our marriage.

So, moving forward, for the benefit of the body of a married couple, we had the hard conversations, so we knew what sacrifices to make for each other. Whether the subject was a big issue or a tiny speck, we sought truth and honesty. It wasn't always easy, but it did seem to get easier over time.

We learned that, even in seemingly little matters, humility paved the path to learning the truth about each other so we could better serve the other's needs.

The outcome has resulted in deeper intimacy and more enjoyment of each other within our marriage. We function as a whole. We've become more prepared to weather the storms that all marriages endure. And we are able to adapt as our family needs grow or change over time.

But for this fellowship to succeed, it required both of us to humbly move toward each other. We couldn't let our individual pride interfere with the goal of our marriage. And, we couldn't do it independently of each other.

- The marriage was strongest when *each* of us decided we belonged to the other.
- The marriage was strongest when *each* of us was willing to sacrifice for the goal of the marriage.
- The marriage was strongest when each of us realized it takes both of us to grow, but the growth wasn't just about ourselves.

It's the same way with your body.

- Your body is strongest when you know each part belongs to (and functions best with) the other parts of your body.
- Your body is strongest when you are willing to sacrifice your short-term desires for the long-term goals of wellness in your body.
- Your body is strongest when you realize it's for you, but it's not just about you.

And, it's the same way with the Lord's Church.

- The church is strongest when you know your body belongs to the other members of the Church.
- The church is strongest when you are willing to sacrifice for the goal of the Church (Kingdom Growth).
- The church is strongest when you realize it takes you, but it isn't just you.

QUICK WORKOUT: PLEASE THINK ABOUT AND ANSWER THE QUESTIONS BELOW.

Which of the above bullet points impact you the most?

_____

_____

_____

In what way?

_____

_____

_____

How to Revive Body Life

DAY 1

Human Body Wellness

In the previous chapters I discussed how Romans 12:1-3 serves as a framework for the way our bodies should be used, and that Christ is the example to follow. When we give our bodies to God as a living and holy sacrifice, it becomes an intimate form of worship. It's also an active demonstration of our obedient commitment to relinquish control of our mind, will and body to God through the Holy Spirit indwelling in us.

As we've seen, living as a holy sacrifice is pleasing to the Lord, but it also helps us improve our lives. We are able to reset our priorities, renew our thinking, transform our behavior, apply it to our self-care, and overcome temptations that interfere with our wellness.

All of these can lead us to think taking care of ourselves should be easy.

But it isn't.

For most people, self-care is difficult. And for people who have been given the spiritual gift of service, it's especially challenging.

People who serve in ministry, non-profit organizations, or care-giving – whether paid or unpaid – are 'can-do kids.' They usually have type A personalities and won't stop until they literally drop. These are not the people who you see in the spa on a weekly basis. They give up and sacrifice (sometimes everything) for the people they love. So, of these people, I believe most of those who are Christians, have already committed to living as a holy sacrifice.

To the point of exhaustion.

As believers, all of us have the capacity to give our bodies as a living sacrifice to serve the Lord, and at our church to expand the Lord's kingdom. But for some of us, if we are not careful, our calling to serve others can become an idol. An idol that has the power to crush us.

I believe that the reason you are reading this book is because you have a calling for service. So, I want to refer back to Romans 12:3 for just one last point before we move on to Romans 12:4 and 5. We need to have a tough conversation so that true fellowship can be enjoyed by all.

And you need to know it, I mean, truly understand it, so you can live out the last point:

You cannot serve indefinitely. You cannot serve without the Holy Spirit. You must rest.

Recall Romans 12:3:

For by the grace given me I say to every one of you: Do not think of yourself more highly than you ought, but rather think of yourself with sober judgment, in accordance with the faith God has distributed to each of you.

I've mentioned this verse twice already, and wrote that *Paul's words remind us to not boast about our gifts, not to covet another's gifts and also not to under-use them. We are also instructed to use our gifts for God's glory because He knows what is best for us. Our gifts come from God, and they are to be used for His purpose. To do this, we have to remain humble. To not be humble to God, puts us in a position where we think we know what is best.*[45]

People like us, who have a calling to serve, generally do not boast about our gifts. But, we are really bad about doing something else. We forget to think of ourselves with sober judgment, and then we forget to take care of *all of the parts of our body.*

People who serve are strong in their faith.

I know you. You recognize the needs around you. You lean on the Lord spiritually. You spend time in the Word. You love others because the Lord loves you.

People who serve do try to take care of their body.

I see you. You work hard to take care of your body. You may be thinking you need to take better care of yourself. You may even be actively working on eating healthier, relieving stress, or getting a little exercise. The physical symptoms you experience drive you to do these things – but only after you finish serving or taking care of others.

But people who serve are not doing a good job at taking care of their emotional or mental health.

I feel you. I've been where you are – I've done what you do. You underestimate your need for rest. And you overestimate your emotional strength.

But, you are only human.

So, you must rest.

Now, of course, we all have to deal with short-term emergencies. What I'm talking about here is your long-term service. Without proper rest and sleep, your emotions – and your inner critic – become louder. Without rest, you will not have the emotional or mental strength to ignore the lies you tell yourself.

So, eventually, maybe without you even knowing it, you begin serving on just your human abilities.

You will not stay well serving independent of the Holy Spirit.

Your body is strongest when you know each part belongs to (and functions best with) the other parts of your body. When you provide your body – and your emotions – the proper rest, your entire body (and mind) can be stronger to serve the Lord.

Your body is strongest when you are willing to sacrifice your desires for the goal of the wellness of your body. When you recognize that your desire to skip rest is driven by lies coming from a tired mind, you can be wise and rest even when you want to keep pushing yourself to the point of physical and mental exhaustion.

Your body is strongest when you realize it's for you, but not just about you.

> *All Scripture is God-breathed and is useful for teaching, rebuking, correcting and training in righteousness, so that the servant of God may be thoroughly equipped for every good work*
> (2 Timothy 3:16-17).

In other words, serving is only serving when you share Christ.

The gift of service requires strong faith, so understand your human limits. When you recognize that your gift of service is not a tool to make you invincible, you learn how to use your faith to see the truth, and thrive – not just survive – in your calling.

You were never meant to provide service for the Lord on just your human abilities.

So, I beg you to stop living this way.

QUICK WORKOUT: PLEASE THINK ABOUT AND ANSWER THE QUESTIONS BELOW.

How often do you find yourself taking care of or serving others when you are exhausted?

_____

_____

_____

Prayerfully reflect on these times. What negative messages does your inner critic say to you that convinces you not to rest?

_____

_____

_____

DAY 2

Church Body Wellness

You and I are a crucial part of Christ's church.

> *For just as each of us has one body with many members,*
> *and these members do not all have the same function, so*
> *in Christ we, though many, form one body, and each*
> *member belongs to all the others* (Romans 12:4-5).

The context of Paul's text is essential for us because we need to understand that we are each just one small part of the whole. Our body is one part of the church body. The church functions at its greatest when all of the church people perform at their best and through a unified existence. When we *all* trust Christ with our bodies and our spiritual gifts, we produce the fruit of kingdom growth.

Christ's church vision is shared in Ephesians.

> *He makes the whole body fit together perfectly. As each*
> *part does its own special work, it helps the other parts*
> *grow, so that the whole body is healthy and growing and*
> *full of love* (Ephesians 4:16)(NLT).[46]

From this we can draw the following conclusions:

- Our self-care can impact our wellness.
- Our wellness affects our ability to share our gifts with the church body.

- The Church's wellness impacts the service provided to the community (and world).

When we interfere with the wellness of the church body (because we don't feel like taking good care of ourselves), we can impede the mission of the Church and the advancement of God's kingdom.

Our gifts are, ultimately, for the benefit of the Church. It's more than just you or me in the church, but, friend, I mean that in a good way! As a follower of Christ, we have the honor of being a part of the church body through our faith, obedience and service.

Serving God as a holy and living sacrifice enables us to use our gifts to our highest ability, regardless of our age or health status. The church will always need people to serve, people to pray, people to give, people to evangelize, all of which can be done at varying degrees. When all of us work towards being at our greatest state of wellness, *and* use our gifts at our most exceptional ability, we as the church function at our highest capacity.

But we struggle if we do not fellowship with the Lord. We forget the points I mentioned above and then run into problems because we:

a. Put too much emphasis on our gifts and think that they make us better than others.
b. Hide or refuse to use our gifts.
c. Allow untruth and sin to consume our hearts. Sin interferes with how we use our gift(s) without the Holy Spirit.
d. Are not united with the church body (discussed in the next section).

Some of us struggle with (a) putting too much emphasis on the value of our gifts for ourselves. We forget or ignore that we received our gifts to glorify the Lord and to use in His Church. Our gift does not make us better than another body member. Thinking we are better than others causes strife in the church and interferes with the health of the congregation. Humility is the critical component.

The apostle Peter speaks about humility within Christians, "Finally, all of you, be like-minded, be sympathetic, love one another, be compassionate and humble" (1 Peter 3:8).

Next, some of us struggle with (b), using our gifts too little. When we refuse to use our gifts or decide that our gifts are not worthy, we affect the growth, health, and wellness of the church. We are telling God that the gifts He gave us are not worthy of the church.

Jesus describes our gifts as light and tells us He *wants* us to use them.

> *"No one lights a lamp and then puts it under a basket. Instead, a lamp is placed on a stand, where it gives light to everyone in the house. In the same way, let your good deeds shine out for all to see, so that everyone will praise your heavenly Father"* (Matthew 5:15-16)(NLT).[47]

The sharing of our spiritual gifts builds the church up for this very task.

Matthew Henry in his Commentary says this of the Church: "The Church serves as the candlesticks and we, as Christians, serve as the light for the candlestick. The light is for the world to see, through our service, good works and the sharing of the gospel."[48]

But, to address my third point, we can struggle (c) when we allow untruth and sin to consume our hearts. Sin interferes with how we use our gift(s) without the Holy Spirit.

The church is strongest when we are willing to sacrifice for the goal of the Church (Kingdom Growth).

Although living as a holy sacrifice as a form of worship is pleasing to God and allows us to use our gifts to the maximum regardless of our health, we can still easily be pulled away from this worship style. Sometimes, we just get impatient with God's ways and we desire an 'easier way.' Or, we might lean on our worldly knowledge, perceptions, and experiences to drive our decisions for our self-care. We look towards the *new and improved* lifestyles in our culture. We find other ways that seem better, quicker, cheaper, more comfortable, more convenient and with less self-sacrifice. We are swiftly and quickly swayed not to trust God.

As I discussed earlier, being in control is an idol for many of us. We idolize being in charge so much we even want to be in charge of God's church! Perhaps even more so, is the *appearance* of being in control. We want others to know about our control in the church. It feeds our nature that we do not need God for anything, especially when it comes to our bodies.

This is sin. And sin can remove the 'breath' from the church.

"The most common reference to the Spirit of God in both the Old and New Testaments is breath," says Robert L. Perry in his book *Congregational Wellness Help for Broken Churches.*[49] "An unhealthy church is one in which the breath of the Spirit has ceased to flow. The congregation does what it does in its own strength and by its own means." In other words, it serves and functions only with human capabilities.[50]

Sacrificing for kingdom growth can't happen if we focus only on ourselves.

It can't happen if we don't properly value our spiritual gifts.

And, it can't happen without the Spirit.

We have a responsibility to bring healing and wellness to our community on a daily basis. The Church cannot serve the community if it focuses only on its own survival.

QUICK WORKOUT: PLEASE THINK ABOUT AND ANSWER THE QUESTIONS BELOW.

When it comes to sharing your spiritual gifts at church, which of the three ways (a), (b) or (c) do you struggle with the most?

_____

_____

_____

Spend a few moments in quiet reflection. In what ways do you like to 'be in control' at church?

_____

_____

_____

DAY 3

Unite through the Spirit

We have an Almighty God who has given us an almighty mission. It's huge! Our mission, if done well, brings God joy and broadens His kingdom. This process occurs by design, so we function at our best for the Church. And this design adds to congregational wellness and growth.

As followers of Christ, we have the honor of being included in the Church body through our faith, obedience, spiritual gifts, and service. And, we have a responsibility to be unified within the church.

> *For the Kingdom of God is not just a lot of talk; it is living by God's power* (1 Corinthians 4:20) (NLT).[51]

Unity is an expectation of the church members. The Holy Spirit can accomplish great works when the church body is unified.

The disciples of the early church loved each other, and this impacted the speed of its growth. Remember during the infancy of the church how rapidly the membership was growing (see Acts 4)? Matthew Henry's Commentary states, "How pleasant it was to see how the *multitude of those that believed* were of one heart, and of one soul, and there was no such thing as discord nor division among them." Henry further comments about the many, many different ages, tempers, conditions and personalities that unified and blended together in harmony and unison. The new believers were likely strangers to each other prior to receiving Christ. They may have come from different religious sects and communities, but all these background differences faded after they came together through Christ.[52]

The church was healthy and well because the people were united through the Spirit, and the kingdom advanced when members shared their spiritual gifts. Scripture guides us to unity in the church. Recall Romans 12:5 as we discussed briefly in chapter 5, *"so we, though many, are one body in Christ, and individually members one of another."*

The church is strongest when you realize it takes you, but it isn't just you.

Paul wrote about this again to the Ephesians, *"Make every effort to keep yourselves united in the Spirit, binding yourselves together with peace"* (Ephesians 4:3-4)(NLT).[53] A definition of peace is "a state of mutual harmony between people or groups, especially personal relations." When the church is united, it presents a consistent arrangement of its parts to the community.

In other words, it's recognizable. It's seen.

It IS light.

And Paul instructs the Colossians in even more detail in Chapter 3.

> *And let the peace that comes from Christ rule in your hearts. For as members of one body you are called to live in peace. And always be thankful. Let the message about*

Christ, in all its richness, fill your lives. Teach and counsel each other with all the wisdom he gives. Sing psalms and hymns and spiritual songs to God with thankful hearts. And whatever you do or say, do it as a representative of the Lord Jesus, giving thanks through him to God the Father (Colossians 3:15-17)(NLT).[54]

It's driven by the peace of Christ and shared through our gratitude.

The Book of Acts provides a clear picture of the unity in Christ's early church.

All the believers were united in heart and mind. And they felt that what they owned was not their own, so they shared everything they had. The apostles testified powerfully to the resurrection of the Lord Jesus, and God's great blessing was upon them all (Acts 4:32-33) (NLT).[55]

We all want to belong to a healthy and united church.

We should all want to BE a healthy and united church.

QUICK WORKOUT: PLEASE THINK ABOUT AND ANSWER THE QUESTIONS BELOW.

Describe a time when you experienced unity in the church.

_____

_____

_____

What are common traps church members can fall into which interferes with unity in the church?

_____

_____

_____

Spend time in prayer. What traps interfere with your ability to unite in the church?

DAY 4

Serve through the Spirit

A unified church creates a pulse that is palpable to the people in the community.

People are suffering and need Jesus. Right now, whether around the corner or on the other side of the world, there is a great need for Christians to unify, be active, and have the capability to put our 'boots on the ground' in order to carry out Christ's mission.

And, sadly, we do not have to look far to see the suffering: we can see it in our community. It's not difficult to find opportunities to serve and improve the wellness of our communities. In fact, most of the areas that we live in have overwhelming needs, needs you can't ignore. In any given community you will find needs to help people who are sick, hungry, living in poverty, homeless, dealing with addiction, grieving, struggling with low wages, victims of crime, sold into human trafficking, and many other situations or atrocities.

Jesus reminds us that we will always have the poor (and the associated problems) among us (see John 12:8) when he references God's command in Deuteronomy 15:11, *"There will always be poor people in the land. Therefore, I command you to be openhanded toward your fellow Israelites who are poor and needy in your land."*

Some of these people are believers. Many, many of the people who are struggling *are not* believers.

To that reality, Jesus says, "*The harvest is plentiful but the workers are few. Ask the Lord of the harvest, therefore, to send out workers into his harvest field*" (Matthew 9:37-38).

We feel the urgency to serve the community and aim for wellness in the areas we live. In fact, it squeezes us from both sides of the lifespan to do more. Communities all over the world are in desperate need of service from a unified Church.

As you've read through most of this book, I believe one of the biggest reasons there are few workers is because Christians do not take good care of themselves and they're not ready for the mission of the Great Commission. But I also think there is intense pressure that is felt by the workers who do see the needs.

Now all glory to God, who is able, through his mighty power at work within us, to accomplish infinitely more than we might ask or think! (Ephesians 3:20)

However, the urgency that comes from the Lord does not steer us to look inward. When we sense an urgency that leads us to focus on ourselves, it is not from the Lord. It's the beginning of burnout. Burnout is a common experience and a risk of serving in ministry. It's easy to spot once you are experiencing severe burnout, but it's not really easy to explain how to prevent or manage it when it first begins. It's not always a long-term experience; that's a myth we all believe.

Burnout can happen quickly, especially to people like us – people who serve and take care of others. You see, I think there are times when we use our gifts of service for our own use even outside the church. I also think there are times when the Spirit knows it's time for us to rest and stops prompting us. Our harvest was enough for that day.

But we ignore it. Because people like us don't quit. We don't give up easily. We continue to serve or take care of the people we love.

And then we ignore the emotional warnings.

The cynicism
The resentment
The irritability
The lack of joy

Friends, just because we can push ourselves in survival mode, doesn't mean we should keep ourselves there.

We need to listen to our emotional cues. Because, albeit sometimes in a negative way, they will tell us we're serving on our own power. They will show us when the Spirit is no longer with us. When we are serving without a 'breath.'

My dear friend, we need to pay attention to this when it happens. Because we won't get through it well on our human abilities. Rest when it's time to rest. Yes, your body will last longer than your emotions. So, don't wait for your body to be exhausted. Instead, watch for the change of focus. Recognize when your mind has turned away from the Spirit.

Watch for when it starts to be about you. Watch when you are tired *and breathless.*

And then rest.

QUICK WORKOUT: PLEASE THINK ABOUT AND ANSWER THE QUESTIONS BELOW.

What signs do you notice when you are 'serving' in survival mode?

_____

_____

_____

Have you ever served to the point of burnout?

_____

_____

_____

Prayerfully commit to listening for the prompting of the Spirit to serve and _also_ rest.

_____

_____

_____

DAY 5

Grace

My friend, we are at the end of this study!

After studying Romans 12:1-5 for so long, and writing all of this to you, I had the hardest time deciding how to wrap up. I sense the Lord wants me to talk about that intangible quality called grace.

Based on my surveys of people who feel called to take better care of themselves, I know the top three reasons people do not perform self-care are:

1. Lack of motivation or interest
2. Lack of time or prioritization
3. Feeling of unworthiness to deserve self-care

I feel I've addressed these issues and provided Scripture-based solutions to these problems.

Yet, I have not been able to eloquently describe the 'Church in action.' But, in a way, that only God can orchestrate when I had to go out of town for my sibling's wedding with less than 300 words to write to finish this book, God showed me the answer.

After my brother got married in another city, he and his family followed us home eight hours so I could mind their kids while they enjoyed a three-day honeymoon in a nearby resort. On the last day, four days after the wedding, my 41-year-old new sister-in-law collapsed walking into a mini-golf facility. She was taken by ambulance to a local hospital where it was determined she had suffered a stroke. Her left side was paralyzed. Thankfully she arrived at the hospital in time to receive a drug to minimize or reverse the damage of the stroke (she is expected to make a full recovery). She was in the hospital for five days while we continued to take care of their six-year-old and eighteen month-old daughters.

It was one of the most sad, scary, and *stressful* family events of my life.

My brother's family experienced a tragedy away from home, away from their friends, co-workers, and church family. My immediate family felt the enormous burden to help and serve them. There was so much to do to care for their two children, my family, support my brother and follow along with the care at the hospital. We were all grieving, too. We were just a small family ourselves.

We couldn't quit. We couldn't give up. But we were exhausted, and couldn't do it alone. After one short text to a church friend, my church went into action. Two separate couples went to pray with my brother and sister-in-law at the hospital, my pastor paid a visit, and two other deacons visited and prayed with them. My small group and disciple group prayed for them. A friend came over to love on me and let me vent when I was exhausted.

Another friend offered a hot meal (that fed us for days!), a circle of additional friends prayed for us, and church members I didn't even know offered prayers for my sister-in-law.

Our church held ALL OF US up!

An adequate description of the 'Church in action' cannot be described just from the perspective of the people who are serving. Yes, the Church will definitely lift up the suffering in the community. But a Church that is united and well – for the purpose of the kingdom, can hold up those who are serving the suffering in the community at the same time.

You see, what you need to understand is that offering your body as a living sacrifice to serve and worship the Lord requires a delicate balance. It's the balance of knowing when to offer the grace of Christ to others and knowing when to accept the grace of Christ for yourself.

QUICK WORKOUT: PLEASE THINK ABOUT AND ANSWER THE QUESTIONS BELOW.

Are you willing to accept grace for yourself when it's needed?

_____

_____

_____

In what ways do you need to accept the grace of Christ for yourself more?

_____

_____

_____

A Promise from God

It's a delicate balance between being ready and capable to serve when the Holy Spirit nudges us, and the act of serving without the Holy Spirit and going beyond the Lord's expectation on our human strength.

We need to stay in fellowship with the Lord to keep us balanced and in the right place. And, the Lord promises victory when we fear Him.

> *But for you who fear my name, the Sun of Righteousness will rise with healing in his wings. And you will go free, leaping with joy like calves let out to pasture. On the day when I act, you will tread upon the wicked as if they were dust under your feet, says the Lord of Heaven's Armies* (Malachi 4:2-3) (NLT).[56]

You were never meant to serve the Lord with just your human abilities, and neither was the Church. His Church is strongest when you realize it takes you, but it's more than just you. Stay in fellowship with the Lord and strive to be a united church. Work together so the body has a continuous breath. Remember to *understand* the Lord's mercy and grace.

RECAP

How do you Revive Body Life?

- Human Body Wellness
- Church Body Wellness
- Unite through the Spirit
- Serve through the Spirit
- Grace

I pray this prayer over you as you consider moving forward with a commitment to live your life as a holy sacrifice:

May you the righteous one flourish like a palm tree,
may you grow like a cedar of Lebanon;
planted in the house of the LORD,
may you flourish in the courts of our God.
You will still bear fruit in old age,
you will stay fresh and green,
proclaiming, "The LORD is upright;
he is my Rock, and there is no wickedness in him"
(Psalm 92:12-15).

My friend, *you have been chosen* to be part of the Lord's church body. Your calling, gifts, and passions are valuable! The Lord has people lined up for you to serve right now. Step forward in faith. You can do this! I believe in you. I believe in the power of the Holy Spirit, which allows me to serve the Lord at my greatest level of wellness, and it can be the same for you. Go forward in obedience. I bid you farewell and encourage you to "seek first his kingdom and his righteousness, and all these things will be given to you as well" (Matthew 6:33).

Epilogue

Thank you for reading this Bible study. I pray you've found something in my story that will bless you. I've been living as a holy sacrifice for almost eight years, and it's difficult to articulate how many positive changes and 'WOW moments' have occurred for my family and me. I have so much to celebrate!

Remember all of the candy I used to eat? I tell you what; the Lord helped me kick that sugar addiction! I still love candy (and eat a piece of *Dove Dark Chocolate* almost every day). I also occasionally buy some of my favorite holiday candy to enjoy (just 2-3 pieces a day depending on the size and only one bag!) But here's the thing, candy doesn't control me. I don't go to candy to find peace and comfort anymore. I go to the Lord, who is always there for me!

I routinely bring my self-care into my morning quiet time. I pray through a list of self-care related scripture verses and ask the Lord to give me strength, wisdom, or peace as it is needed. (You can see and download my list of verses at https://mylifenurse.com/5-verses-to-help-you-focus-on-self-care/.) I also request self-care related prayer from others-which is uncomfortable sometimes. Like you - I don't want to sound like a complainer. However, I share my needs with a small group of trusted friends who understand and 'get me.' And wonderfully, some of my friends have shared their self-care needs with me. I feel honored to pray for another's self-care requests.

People frequently ask how I exercise, what I eat, and what eating plan my family follows. I prefer walking and running, yoga, and weight-training. In general, we follow a Mediterranean Diet. We eat a lot of fresh fruit and vegetables - most of them raw. We have some favorite meatless recipes (with vegetable spaghetti squash, zucchini, or roasted vegetables), and we eat a large variety of grains. For protein options, we eat mostly peanut butter, hummus, salmon, tuna, chicken, shrimp, steak, and even hamburgers.

I abstain from eating wheat during the weekdays (i.e., bread and pasta). I have recently started to follow an intermittent fasting schedule where I fast nightly for 14-15 hours. I also occasionally perform a 24-hour fast. I fast for spiritual reasons (nothing to do with an eating plan) - primarily when I am waiting to hear from the Lord or as part of prayer activity. While I still don't get *excited* about feeling a call to fast, I will admit I'm no longer fearful and readily do so.

So, am I perfect? Um, no. I still have areas where I struggle. For example, I frequently wanted to use finalizing this book as an excuse not to exercise over the last two-and-a-half years. For accountability, I asked my friend to tell me to fess up to whether I've been compliant with exercise when she does my nails (which is my pampering reward for taking care of myself!).

But, more than anything else, I celebrate how the Lord has turned my prayer life into a way to feel the prompting of the Holy Spirit so I could be a Godlier wife, mom, friend, sister, and daughter. My trust grew as my fellowship with the Lord became more intimate. As I continued to walk forward in obedience to research and write this book, the Lord equipped me with whatever I needed in my life *at every step*.

I have learned how to better ignore the fear of the unknown and embrace walking forward — even though I was uncomfortable, and even when it felt inelegant. But, because I stepped forward in obedience, my home and family life has been blessed in ways I never imagined. We have genuine peace in our family life-no matter the circumstances.

As I close, please know that I want these victories for you too. And friend, I genuinely believe you can have them.

Now, take good care of yourself and go change the world.

Let's Keep in Touch

Thank you for letting me share my self-care journey with you. I'd love to hear about yours! I invite you to join me at mylifenurse.com where we can keep in touch through my email newsletter. You can subscribe at https://mylifenurse.com/my-life-nurse-newsletter/.

Also, if you would like to continue to dig into faith-driven self-care, you can find additional materials here: https://mylifenurse.com/faith-driven-self-care-materials/.

If you enjoyed *The Self-care Impact: Motivation and Inspiration for Wellness*, you may like my other writing, too. In addition to subscribing to my newsletter, you can also find encouraging and motivating messages on my blog at https://mylifenurse.com/blog/.

Finally, I pray you enjoy the Lord's promises of offering your body as a living sacrifice on a daily basis.

FREE Bible Study Checklist

If you did not see the link to the FREE Bible Study Checklist & Workbook in the beginning of this Bible Study, you can go to the link below to print a list of the suggested actions I wrote in this Bible study.

You can find them https://mylifenurse.com/self-care-impact-free-checklist/.

Acknowledgments

There is no way I could have written this book without the encouragement, instructional guidance, and assistance from all of the amazing people on this list. I am incredibly blessed to have so many inspirational people in my life.

I have to start with giving a huge thank you to my husband, *Richard*. This poor man has listened to me talk about writing this book for eight years, which honestly should award him sainthood! He teases that my projects become his projects but, truly, this book is an effort from both of us. Honey, I am so grateful for your encouragement and voice of reason when I needed it, and I love you more every day.

I also deeply appreciate my children *Joshua* and *Sara*. I love being your mom and appreciate your continuous support. I am so proud of both of you and love you so very much.

It is wonderful to know that my parents, siblings, father-in-law, and sister-in-laws are my continual cheerleaders and supporters. I am very blessed.

I have to give a special mention to my friend and mentor, *Jim Stovall*, thank you for sharing your wisdom — and humor — when I most needed it. You have a way with words and your timing is simply impeccable. Thank you also for writing the forward of this book.

And, *Fleur Vaz,* wow, I am so grateful the Lord brought us together. Your editing skills are magical; you made my writing into a legible book! I thank you for sharing not only your professional expertise and gift of editing, but also your ideas, prayers, and suggestions. Your generosity will bring blessings to anyone who reads the book! Thank you!

For the rest of the people* on this list, I can't express enough my gratitude to you. Your words, actions, and encouragement came at the very times I needed it. You have no idea how helpful you were!

To *Lacey Eddington,* thank you for listening to every last detail about this book and your ongoing encouragement and advice. You were there from the beginning and lasted to the end. You are a very special friend.

To *Susan Grogan,* thank you for telling me how my face lit up when I spoke about my book vision. Your words gave me confidence at one of my most fearful moments on this journey.

To *Debbie Yokum,* thank you for telling me I couldn't run away from the task God was calling me to do. I needed to hear that right at that time.

To *Andrea Lennon,* thank you for your coaching and advice. I remember your words, "speak boldly" and strive to do so whenever I talk about my book. You are an inspiration and I appreciate the wisdom you shared.

To *Gina Horkey*, thank you for your incredible course, (affiliate link) '30 Days or Less to Freelance Writing Success' - https://horkeyhandbook.samcart.com/referral/30-Days-or-Less-to-Freelance-Writing-Success/603785. Taking your course(s) gave me the writing and technical skills and the confidence I needed to start writing and walking in obedience. Watching you soar to entrepreneurial success has been a privilege. But getting to know you was the icing on the cake.

To *Sue Edmonds*, thank you for helping me with...everything! Your friendship, discipleship, and vulnerability have been priceless to me.

To *Kate Kail*, thank you for meeting me for our 'entrepreneur coffee meetings.' It was such a help to talk to someone who was walking a very similar journey. You inspire me.

To *Jennifer Nagle*, you are the wind beneath my wing. Thank you for your encouragement, the kicks in the pants as needed, and always believing in me - even when I didn't.

To *Lynda Schibler*, thank you for your advice. Your experience and expertise crosses over many specialties, and for that I have been blessed repeatedly through your wisdom and friendship.

To *Ruth Soukup*, my blogging mentor and hero, thank you for all of your teachings. I love all of your products but especially the Living Well Planner!

To *Cindi Boston,* thank you for your friendship and professional insights. I appreciate your personal coaching and connecting me with the right people. I am so proud of your fearless obedience.

To *Brandi Melvin,* thank you for your encouragement and friendship. And, it's wonderful to find someone of similar humor!

To *P.K. Hinkle,* thank you for allowing me to present my draft Bible study to a small group. Because you treated it like it was the 'real deal', I felt like it was too.

To *Charlene Anderson,* thank you for helping with all of the presentation tasks and most importantly your encouragement and prayers.

To *Sr. Elizabeth Weiler,* thank you for deep, lively and encouraging conversations. I deeply treasure our long friendship!

To *Pastor John Black,* thank you for your advice, guiding me through various theology and commentaries, and finding the perfect references and books for my research!

To my disciple group, *Bekah Choi, Brenda Horner, Brianne McCormick* and *Vanece Williams,* thank you for your relentless encouragement and committed support!

To *Tracy Lipscomb,* thank you for reading my Bible study before it was edited and sharing such kind feedback.

ACKNOWLEDGMENTS

To my church family thank you for your prayers, support and encouragement. And, to those who attended a weekly Bible study presentation of pieces of my book, *Mary Miller, Christy Yoakum, Norma Taube, Pam Harp, Tamara Cram, Sarah Mayfield, Stacey Hurley, Susie Scroggins, Wes Scroggins, Cindy Mickan, Kathy Lanham, Melissa Spake, Dina Davis, Laura Davis, Sherry Raney, Tammie Knight,* and *Laura Doyle,* thank you for coming back every week. Your feedback was greatly appreciated and implemented! But your reassurance helped me continue my forward momentum!

To *Vicky Thomas,* thank you so much for outlining the publishing process and sharing your resources and wisdom with me.

To my blogging partners, *Kimberly Joy Evers, Tammy Rotzoll* and *Timberley Gray,* thank you for your inspiration, encouragement and wisdom. You ladies are amazing and I'm so grateful to have been able to meet you in person and be on this journey together.

To my online accountability partners, *Kimberly McCann* and *Katie Deckert,* thank you for your ongoing encouragement and keeping my toes to the line! I appreciate your candor balanced with encouragement at just the right times. I sure hope I do the same for you.

To my former mastermind group members (and now friends), *Ally King, Sarah Belanger, Kristine Bessell, Alicia Hunter, Diona Culbertson, Nancy Mock, Nicole Hermens* thank you for all of your encouragement, ideas, instructions, and advice.

To my beta readers, *Sue Edmonds, Danielle Hartsell, Jodi Stevenson, Pamela Stafford,* and *Ifeoma Samuel,* a special, heartfelt thank you for taking your precious time to read the book (or parts of it) and give me feedback and suggestions.

To my entire book launch team, thank you for your encouragement and precious help during my book launch.

Finally, to all of the subscribers on my blog, *My Life Nurse*, thank you for reading my writing and sending notes of encouragement, appreciation, and support as we've shared this journey together. Sending love to you all.

*I am sure I'm forgetting some important people so I started a list at https://mylifenurse.com/the-self-care-impact-book-thank-you-list/ and will update it annually. If you know of someone I missed (or if I missed *you*) please email me at Lisa@mylifenurse.com so I can update the list.

Notes

I have included a detailed list of references and notes in this section. Every effort has been made to properly note the citations used while researching this book. However, because my research took several years, literature and websites can change over time or edits may be needed. Furthermore, if a mistake is noted (whether attributing an idea or quote to the wrong person or overlooking credit where due) I am interested in correcting the problem. Please contact me at Lisa@mylifenurse.com if you have changes or see entries that need corrections.

Chapter 1:

1. "Definition of Health | Dictionary.Com."
   Www.Dictionary.Com, 2020,
   www.dictionary.com/browse/health?s=t. (emphasis added).
2. "Definition of Wellness | Dictionary.Com."
   Www.Dictionary.Com, 2020,
   www.dictionary.com/browse/wellness?s=t. (emphasis added).
3. Witmer, J. A. Romans. In J. F. Walvoord & R. B. Zuck (Eds.), The Bible Knowledge Commentary: An Exposition of the Scriptures. Vol. 2, Victor Books, 1985. p. 487.
4. Ibid.
5. Black, John. South Gate Baptist Church, Circa 2018, Springfield, MO. Weekly sermon.

6. Witmer, J. A. Romans. In J. F. Walvoord & R. B. Zuck (Eds.), The Bible Knowledge Commentary: An Exposition of the Scriptures. Vol. 2, Victor Books, 1985. p. 487.
7. Ibid.
8. Paul, Marla. *Religious Young Adults Become Obese by Middle Age.* Northwestern U, 2011, www.northwestern.edu/newscenter/stories/2011/03/religious-young-adults-obese.html Paragraph 5. Accessed 18 Feb. 2020.
9. Cline, Krista, and Ferraro, Kenneth. "Does Religion Increase the Prevalence and Incidence of Obesity in Adulthood?" *Journal for the Scientific Study of Religion.* www.ncbi.nlm.nih.gov/pmc/articles/PMC3358928/ 2006 Jun; 45(2): 269-281. Table 2. Accessed 18 Feb 2020.
10. Stoll, Scott. "Fat in Church." *Fox News Opinion*, 4 Jan 2013, www.foxnews.com/opinion/fat-in-church. Accessed 18 Feb 1010.

Chapter 2:
11. Walvoord, John F., and Roy B. Zuck, Dallas Theological Seminary. *The Bible Knowledge Commentary: An Exposition of the Scriptures.* Wheaton, IL: Victor Books, 1985.
12. Ibid.
13. Easley, Kendell, *The Gospel Project for Students: God Delivers,* Leader Guide, vol. 4. No. 2, Lifeway Christian Resources, 2015, page 123.
14. Benner, Jeff, *Genesis 1:27,* www.ancient-hebrew.org/40_genesis1.html Accessed 26 March 2015. (URL no longer available).

15. Hybels, B., 2010. *The Power Of A Whisper*. Grand Rapids, Mich.: Zondervan. p. 252.
16. "New Living Translation (NLT) - Version Information - BibleGateway.Com." *Biblegateway.Com*, BibleGateway, 2015, www.biblegateway.com/versions/New-Living-Translation-NLT-Bible/.
17. Wiersbe, Warren. "Our Relationship to God." *Warren Wiersbe BE Bible Study Series,* Romans 12: 1-2, The Warren Wiersbe BE from *Bible Gateway, www.biblegateway.com/passage/?search=romans+12%3A2&version=NIV*. Accessed 18 Feb 2020.
18. Carpenter, Eugene. *"General Principle." Asbury Bible Commentary*, Romans 12: 1-2, from *BibleGateway*, emphasis added, https://www.biblegateway.com/passage/?search=Romans+12%3A+2&version=NIV. 1992. Accessed 18 Feb 2020.
19. Ibid.
20. Henry, Matthew. *"Verses 1-21." Henry Bible Commentary*, Romans 12: 1-2, from *Bible Gateway*, emphasis added, https://www.biblegateway.com/passage/?search=romans+12%3A+1-2&version=NIV. Accessed 18 Feb 2020.

Chapter 3:

21. Varner, Robert, South Gate Baptist Church, circa 2017, Springfield, MO, Personal Communication.
22. Washer, Paul. "A Living and Holy Sacrifice", citing Romans 12:1-2, *YouTube*.uploaded by The Master's Seminary, 11 Oct 2013, www.youtube.com/watch?v=o6hYEqpQxds&t=6s
23. Wallis, Arthur. *God's Chosen Fast A Spiritual and Practical Guide to Fasting*. 1968. CLC Publications, 2015, p. 34.

24. Ibid. p. 82, emphasis added.

25. Ibid. p. 53.

26. Ibid. p. 46.

27. Ibid. p. 26.

28. Ibid. p. 52.

29. "Involving the Community in Your Decisions (Romans 12:1–3)" *Theology of Work Body Commentary* Romans 12: 1-3, from *Bible Gateway*, https://www.biblegateway.com/passage/?search=romans+12%3A+3&version=NIV. Accessed 18 Feb 2020.

30. Dillow, L., 2014. *Satisfy My Thirsty Soul.* Carol Stream, Ill.: Tyndale House Publishers, Inc. p. 102.

Chapter 4

31. Anonymous essay, www.impactingpoverty.org/wp-content/uploads/2014/04/Why-I-Make-Terrible-Decisions-Blog.pdf accessed circa Oct 2014. (URL no longer available).

32. Graham, Billy. "What Does It Mean to Be Poor in Spirit, as Jesus Said We Ought to Be?" *Billy Graham Evangelistic Association,* 2018, billygraham.org/answer/what-does-it-mean-to-be-poor-in-spirit-as-jesus-said-we-ought-to-be/. Accessed 18 Feb 2020.

33. Dictionary.com https://www.dictionary.com/

34. Wiersbe, Warren. "Psalm 103." *Warren Wiersbe BE Bible Study Series,* Psalm 103. The Warren Wiersbe BE from *Bible Gateway,* www.biblegateway.com/passage/?search=Psalms+103%3A1-5&version=NIV. Accessed 18 Feb 2020.

35. Unger, Merrill. *What Demons Can Do To Saints. Moody Press,* 1991,Unger, M. and Bubeck, M., 1995. p. 45.

36. Ibid. (p. 49).

37. Ibid. (p. 129).

38. Hybels, B., 2010. *The Power Of A Whisper*. Grand Rapids, Mich.: Zondervan. p. 136.

Chapter 5:

39. Unger, M. and Bubeck, M., 1995. *What Demons Can Do To Saints*. Chicago: Moody Publishers, p.59.

40. Ibid. p. 79.

41. Ibid. p. 61, emphasis added.

42. Ibid. p. 83.

43. Strand, Robert. *Self-Control Nine Fruits of the Spirit, A Devotion Series*. 1999. New Leaf Press, 2009, p. 9-10.

44. "New Living Translation (NLT) - Version Information - BibleGateway.Com." *Biblegateway.Com*, BibleGateway, 2015, https://www.biblegateway.com/versions/New-Living-Translation-NLT-Bible/.

Chapter 6:

45. "Involving the Community in Your Decisions (Romans 12:1–3)" *Theology of Work Body Commentary* Romans 12: 1-3, from *Bible Gateway*, https://www.biblegateway.com/passage/?search=romans+12%3A+3&version=NIV. Accessed 18 Feb 2020.

46. "New Living Translation (NLT) - Version Information - BibleGateway.Com." *Biblegateway.Com*, BibleGateway, 2015, https://www.biblegateway.com/versions/New-Living-Translation-NLT-Bible/.

47. Ibid.

48. Henry, Matthew. "Chapter 5" Henry Bible Commentary, Matthew 5:15, from *Blue Letter Bible* https://www.blueletterbible.org/Comm/mhc/Mat/Mat_005.c om?a=934015 Accessed 18 Feb 2020.
49. Perry, R., 1997. *Congregational Wellness*. Richmond, Va.: Organizational Health Associates. p. 12.
50. Ibid. p. 13.
51. "New Living Translation (NLT) - Version Information - BibleGateway.Com." *Biblegateway.Com*, BibleGateway, 2015, https://www.biblegateway.com/versions/New-Living-Translation-NLT-Bible/.
52. Henry, Matthew. "*Verses 32-27.*" Henry Bible Commentary, Acts 4: 32-33, from *Bible Gateway*, https://www.biblegateway.com/passage/?search=acts+4%3A3 2-33&version=NIV. Accessed 18 Feb 2020.
53. "New Living Translation (NLT) - Version Information - BibleGateway.Com." *Biblegateway.Com*, BibleGateway, 2015, https://www.biblegateway.com/versions/New-Living-Translation-NLT-Bible/.
54. Ibid.
55. Ibid.
56. Ibid.